Running away from home seems like a great idea to thirteen-year-old Billy Steele. He can be free to escape the problems of family and school, finding instead a new, untroubled dream-life on his own in Waikiki.

But Billy is about to discover that dreams don't always turn out as one might expect, and that it's a whole different world when experienced *From The Other Side*.

From The Other Side

Special Textbook-Edition featuring

•enhanced text for vocabulary building

•attractive illustrations

•end-of-book *Glossary*

(176 pages)

Computer Layout:	*Toni Shortsleeve*
Illustrated by:	*Ernest Oshiro*
Cover Design:	*Doug Behrens*

TABLE OF CONTENTS

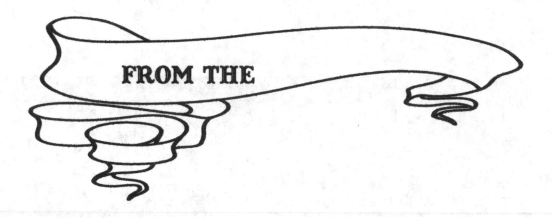

FROM THE

Reading and building key vocabulary is a pleasurable experience when the stories are exciting and the text is challenging.

The enclosed tale is set in the Hawaiian Islands, but the adventures and lessons learned are universal.

Come let the Huckleberry Finn in you escape on a raft of unbounded fantasy and imagination as you embark on a verbally enriching odyssey with characters who will endear themselves to you through their personal and poignant escapades.

Let the journey begin...

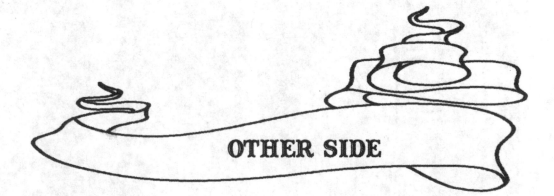

OTHER SIDE

CHAPTER I
Words of Freedom

The stage was alive with the pulse of a billion sounds. Four thousand tongues sang along to the hypnotic beat, erupting in **unison** at each refrain. *Lady M* was there. She could have been anywhere else in the world, but tonight she was really there, singing for four thousand hungry followers, four thousand people who paid ten dollars each to listen to her. The idea of having people pay to see her sent a shiver of delight through Billy Steele. He wondered how *Lady M* must feel? Could anyone really ever expect to feel any higher?

It was time to leave, time to run away. Nobody could stop him now. Not his parents, not the school, not the police. Nobody. This was what Billy had been waiting for. A reason to strike out on his own. No more listening to others, no more restrictions and no more excuses. He'd been waiting for this moment and now he saw the glitter and the hope up there on stage.

"Two hearts, two hearts that beat as one..." The words rushed through his senses like a strong cigarette. They were calling him, **beckoning** him to leave his **bland** existence behind. It was time to stop observing and start moving. He was old enough to decide for himself, and the visions of promise were just too strong and **captivatingly tantalizing** to let slide. Not this time. He'd threatened to leave before, but he could never find enough purpose, enough of a direction to push him over the edge, over the top.

The concert was over. No **encore**, just bright lights turned on and people exiting **mindlessly**, back to their **irrelevant** existence. Colorful shirts whizzed by, *Levi* cords and *Jimmy 'Z* and *Quiksilver* trousers, tight mini-skirts and body shirts. The mass swarmed past him as though all heading for class, going nowhere and trying to look good doing it.

"Stewart," Billy began as he turned to face his thirteen-year-old fellow student and lifelong friend, "what do you think of 'digging'? I mean, really digging out?"

Stewart Simon, his **intimate** blue-eyed friend, stared at him with a look Billy had seen many times before, a look somewhere between disbelief and a dare. "Snicker, you've asked me this so many times this week, I don't know what you want me to say. Like I said before, if you gotta go, you gotta go."

"Yeah, but I really mean it this time. I can't stay here anymore. She was really hot, wasn't she?"

"For sure, Snick, she was the top. Man, I'm gonna put up the biggest poster of her, and I don't care what my sister says. She'll just have to get used to it. Right on the ceiling. How about that, Snick?"

Billy's thoughts drifted from his own **preoccupation** and imagined the huge *Lady M* poster staring down as he woke up in the morning. "Boy, that would be a great way to start off the day. I could see my folks climbing the walls."

They looked smilingly at one another, catching the well-timed **pun**, acting like the best of friends that they really were. They weren't ordinary thirteen-year-old American boys, no matter what adults told them. Billy knew they were special. They lived in Hawaii. Nobody grew up in a **bustling metropolis** like Honolulu and remained just an 'ordinary' kid. There was so much to do, so much to see. And there were too many ideas floating around to just grow up like any other teen in any other town. They were special, and as Billy and Stewart locked eyes they shared with one another the many years of growth they had experienced, each knowing that they had **plumbed** the depths of life's challenges with a reckless **abandon atypical** for boys their own age. Their parents couldn't even begin to guess how much they had accomplished, how much they knew or how they felt, and what **motivated** them to do what they did. Or what they wanted to do.

"Where are you headed now, Snick?" Stewart asked curiously as the crowds around them **dispersed**.

"Oh yeah, I better start thinking about what to do. I really want to dig, far and fast. Can you help me, Stew?" Billy's eyes were still red from earlier in the evening, when he all but cried the house down to finally persuade his dad to let him go to the concert. Every liberty granted to him seemed to require the consent of everyone in the household, a **stifling hindrance** that **grated** on his innermost being which **craved autonomy**. **Cherished** as the only child wasn't as glamorous as others seemed to think. Rather than being showered with generosity, he was instead enslaved with guilt-ridden responsibility accompanied by **tokens** of conditional affection, gifts **lavished** upon him that committed him to a life of **fettered bondage** and **domestic servitude**. He was a prisoner **languishing** within his own castle.

"Billy," Stewart began, changing into a more serious tone, "can't you just live with your folks and not feel that they're chaining you down?"

"Stew, don't come on like that again. Please. I really need your help. I can't stay home. They won't let me do anything, and I'm gonna break if I don't split soon. I tell you, I'm gonna crack."

"Then what do you want me to do? I can't just invite you to my place. Your folks would have a fit. And my folks would probably kick me out if I got them in trouble. You know how parents are."

Stewart was Billy's best friend, best advisor and perhaps the only person he knew who could talk with him and yet not confine him. Stewart's parents were more understanding than his own, yet strict and demanding of respect and responsibility nonetheless. "You're old enough to take care of yourself, son," Stewart's dad told him on his thirteenth birthday, "and if you ever feel that you aren't being treated as a grown-up, you tell us. But you remember that there's a way to act when you're grown up, and we expect it from you."

Stewart's sister wasn't quite so fortunate, being two years older and having experienced enough run-ins with the law to require tighter **reins** by the parents. Stewart was in his folks' favor, a position of honor he valued dearly, a **distinction** he dared not **jeopardize** through **sophomoric puerile** acts of **juvenile indiscretion.**

But Billy was a special friend for Stewart, a person he'd risk his reputation to help. Ever since they'd first noticed one another in the second grade, the two shared in everything, the good times and the bad times. When Billy broke his arm falling off a skateboard, it was Stewart who visited him daily at his house, watching after him and updating him on the latest school events and school gossip.

And Billy would lay his life down for Stewart – that Stewart knew for a fact. When Jack Costa, the ninth-grade neighborhood bully, **confronted** Stewart a year ago in front of the Waikiki *7/Eleven* and demanded money, Billy was there to put out the fire. Billy wasn't big, but his **grit** and determination to help his closest friend overpowered anything that any mighty *Goliath* could **muster.** Unable to **wrest** any funds through **extortion**, Costa backed off, frustrated that his verbal demands were not effective but just as anxious not to make a scene with a **doughty** lad half his size. What Billy lacked in physical **adeptness** he more than made up for in spirit.

Stewart's eyes drifted around as if seeking some answer from the walls of the *Blaisdell Concert Hall.* Why would his closest friend want to just pack up and leave? What really could be the reason? And what could he do to help? It was like the **query** his history teacher had presented to him last week: "How could World War II have been **prevented**?" The question seemed **frivolously moot** and **rhetorical** to him at the time. It had happened fifty years ago, and now someone wanted to know how it could have been avoided. Did it matter anymore? Was there any **relevance** in an issue long past to issues of personal and **contemporary** interest? At the time, Stewart found no relationship between the **heuristic** historical question and the events of his or Billy's **quotidian** activities. But the question didn't seem silly now, as Stewart found himself faced with a similarly **perplexing** problem regarding how to **alter** the course of human events, though of a more personal and specific nature.

What could Stewart do? For the longest time Billy had **coveted** fame, fortune and independence, so what could anyone else now do to change his mind? It would be as impossible as having **strived** to **alter** the events leading up to World War II. There was no way to change the course, but maybe there was a way to **subjugate** the **fanciful** visions which were consuming Billy's thoughts and **compelling** him to act **precipitately.** Nevertheless, taking him to the concert didn't seem to be such a good idea after all, but the damage had been done – the floodgates of freedom were now **enticing** him to enter the **realm** of the unexplored. Yet, if Billy hadn't been with Stewart tonight, where would he be? On the streets somewhere seeking a **salvation** as **illusive** as his **delusory** dreams? Or worse yet, greeting strangers who would promise him everything and give him nothing?

"Let's get out of here, Snick," Stewart resumed. "I've gotta think of what we can do. Let's go to *McDonald's* if they're still open. I think we'd better have a drink or two over this.

"Thanks, Stew," Billy replied. "I trust you a whole lot, brother. You're all I've got."

The words rang through Stewart's mind like a mid-day church-bell, pounding within his **adolescent** head a **deafening tintinnabulation**. Billy put too much trust in people, and Stewart knew he was perhaps the only one who really could understand, or at least listen to what Billy had to say. They were both thirteen, but what they were faced with was no **whimsical notion**. Billy's **resolution** was in **earnest**, and Stewart knew only he alone could **dissuade** his **headstrong comrade** from venturing out into the darkness. Where Billy was headed, it wouldn't matter; he would find his **destiny**, eventually.

"I don't know how I can help," Stewart added as they headed to *McDonald's*. But he knew that the real words should have been "I don't know *if* I can help."

"I've gotta think of what we can do."

CHAPTER II
Unbounded Energies

Billy attended school as usual on Monday, following his routine as though nothing **notable** had occurred over the weekend. Stewart met him on the bus, and the two remained **inseparable** from that moment on, attending four classes together and spending recess and lunch-break discussing typically **temporal** teenage concerns: friends, parents, teachers – and of course, breaking free.

"I'm still going, you know," Billy **interjected** as the ten-minute recess counted down to its final moments. "That concert was the sign. She was singing to me and I could feel her telling me that it's time to take off."

"Snick," his friend replied **soberly**, "she was singing for four thousand other people who all heard the same words. Hey, all she was doing was singing, and you can take it any way you want, anywhere you want to."

"You're wrong, Stew, so wrong. I know what I've gotta do, and I'm gonna do it soon. Real soon." His words were carefully and decisively **crafted**.

Stewart bit his lip as he **contemplated** the abrupt **assessment** he had delivered which he hoped would discourage his **ally** from **decamping**. The **appraisal** had done little more than add **kindling** to the flame for flight. Billy was determined and little could be said to change his mind. Perhaps he'd forget. Perhaps it was best that Stewart simply shift the focus away from the **provocatively incendiary** issue. "Snick, I've gotta go to math class. I'm having a pre-Alg test. Heck, why does Mrs. Enos have to give us a test on Monday? That's really unfair, you know that, Snick?"

"Yeah, I guess so," Billy answered in a distant manner. Stewart knew that the **digressive** comment hadn't **distracted** Billy from his train of thought, but perhaps peace and stability could be restored if the intense discussion had time to cool itself off.

"Well, see ya for lunch, Snick. Hang in there, okay?"

"Sure, Stew. You know I'll hang in there. See you for lunch."

But lunch would be just another confining routine, and Billy was now looking for something or someone to further **whet** his appetite and **incite** him to expand his horizons, someone to serve as a **catalyst** – daring him to prove his manhood by taking that adventurous step beyond. He anxiously headed for his geography class in search of Butch, the perfect friend for the occasion. If anyone could **rouse** him to action, it would surely be the **garrulous** school **malcontent**, the boy who gave great armchair advice at no cost or obligation.

As Billy entered the **forbidding** den of one of his least favorite teachers, he **mulled over** the **likelihood** of **imminent liberation** from the **circumscribed** existence he now found himself entrapped within.

"All right, class, let's settle down." Mrs. Costello gathered her papers together as the class came to a comfortable silence. "I've got your papers here from last week, and I must say I was quite **impressed** by your effort. Billy, quit talking to Butch or I might just change your grade."

A few students chuckled and commented quietly to one another about how school teachers always seem to find a way to add a bit of humiliation even during the most **innocuously** innocent moments of the day. This time, however, Billy wasn't merely passing time with **idle** chatter, and he resented being interrupted at that precise moment.

"Billy, you can count on an F if you keep talking." Mrs. Costello was **flexing** her muscle, as did most teachers when a student tried to assert himself and demand his rights. The **confrontation** was an almost daily event for Billy in most of his classes. He was the student most likely to be sent to the principal, but not for reasons of **belligerence** or **recalcitrance**. He simply seemed to have **unbounded** energies, coming up with ideas which, though not **germane** to class discussions, nevertheless were worthy of **merit**. The previous week he had asked Mr. Zimmerman, the math teacher, why Hitler hated the Jews so much. Zimmerman took the question as a personal **affront** and **unceremoniously** escorted Billy to the office. From that day on, Mr. Zimmerman was given the unlikely nickname of 'Hitler,' a **grim** reminder of his **forefathers' plight** and also of his treatment of Billy, the *Leonardo da Vinci* of the eighth grade. The **outspoken** rebel youngster was always the **maverick**, always doing something or saying something unique, unrestricted, and generally what the teachers would describe as 'uncalled for.'

"Mrs. Costello," Billy **queried** seriously as he glanced up at her from his sixth-row seat, "is it really true that freedom is a state of mind? That being free is like closing your eyes and saying that nothing outside really exists?"

"That's it, young man. No more **tomfoolery** from you. I've heard enough wisecracks. Go straight to the dean's office and tell him what you said." The class began to giggle in spurts. Billy had asked a **probing** question and Costello had reacted as an ignorant **buffoon**, unaware of any significance in the young man's train of thought. Everyone in the class seemed to **fathom** the seriousness of the **spontaneous inquiry**, everyone except the teacher herself.

"Gee, I don't know what I said that bothered you, Mrs. *Abbott*," he added with a **subtle coyness** that **belied** his true recognition of the victorious verbal **volley**. The class erupted into laughter, some of the girls even applauding his **apt** though **flippant** reference to the comedy duo of the black-and-white film era. But Mrs. Costello didn't catch the **gist** and maintained her **stern, astringent countenance**. "You all can get an F, I don't care. You are all just a bunch of animals sometimes. Taking a joke too far is one thing, but you don't even know what you're laughing at." The ignorance of her comment seemed **ludicrous**, and the class quickly calmed down to avoid **antagonizing** her with any further intellectual **forays** that would doubtless be **construed** as **fatuous folly**. The students had **outwitted** the teacher, again. Billy was the source of the **repartee**, yet he was also the target of the **retribution**. Realizing it was a hollow *Pyrrhic* victory, the **paragon** of the **petulant** poster child packed his books while planning his next move.

"I think it's time to 'bag'," he muttered softly to Butch Van Moren as he headed for the aisle.

"Remember what I said," Butch voiced more loudly. "You're safe in the streets."

The hallways **beckoned** him onward as the **ostracized iconoclast** exited the geography class for the final time.

CHAPTER III
The Reminder

"Well, well, well, you're back again so soon," Mr. Stimson **bellowed** in an **indignant air** of **supremacy**. "What did you do this time, huh boy?"

"Well, Mr. Stimson, I guess – "

"Don't give me any of your **insubordinate** back-talk, Mr. Steele. You've been bad-mouthing Mrs. Costello again. Every week you're in here for something or other. What should we do with you, young man?" The question did not **beg** a reply. Mr. Stimson was the dean of discipline, and he knew all the answers. The students were merely receivers of his **scathing rebukes**, nothing more. Billy listened to the **peremptory** verdict.

"After school for an hour, maybe for two? And let's do that for a couple of weeks and see how you like it. Or maybe you want us to just kick your smart butt out of Palmview and into some public school that can't turn you down. Your folks would love that, wouldn't they, Mr. Steele? Are you listening to me, boy?"

Billy's thoughts had drifted out to the safety of the streets, where there were no limits, no threats, nobody there to police a set of undesired rules.

"Uh, yeah, I heard you, Mr. Stimson," he replied almost absent-mindedly. "I mean, whatever you said, I totally agree."

"You don't know how to listen, Mr. Steele. You never did, you never will. You're a waste, just a lousy excuse for a person."

Billy heard that. The **demeaning** words struck a deep chord in his soul, words that tried to force him to **humble submission**, words that sought to make him **grovel** in the dirt and beg for mercy. But Billy had survived humiliation and **intimidation** before, all those times his mom and dad had threatened to punish him for not finishing his homework or for staying out too late. Such **lordly** and **imperious** displays of domination were **nugatory**; they were merely words without substance. His folks **revered** him too much to dare **alienate** him. Every threat led to an apology, every punishment covered up with **remorseful** acts of **remuneration**. Every emotion of parental concern seemed to be padded with guilt, as though they were afraid to admit to themselves and express to him how much they really cared about him. "If only you would once do what you said you'd do, then I'd know for sure," he'd told them in one of his more **lucidly** communicative moments. But his parents didn't understand, and from that day forth Billy left them alone and **conceded** that he would never be understood. He could run away and still they'd never know why.

"Mr. Stimson," he voiced with a **latent fury festering** from within, "nobody ever tells me that I'm no good. Not you, not my parents, nobody."

"Every week you're in here for something or other."

Mr. Stimson cut him short. "Then you do something about it."

"Oh, I will, you can count on that, sir. You can count on that." He left his words a general mystery, awaiting instead the final verdict from the **Joseph Mengele** of Palmview Intermediate & High School.

"I don't know if I should do this, but I'll let you go this time," Stimson concluded compromisingly. It was just like all the other times: meaningless threats lacking **puissance** and **conviction**. In the **guise** of **condescending clemency**, it was clear that nobody possessed the **mettle** to stand by their words.

"Thanks, sir, I really appreciate that" was all that was necessary. It was Billy's **stock** response to **mealymouthed** attempts by **pusillanimous poltroons** to assert themselves and hardly meant the thankfulness which the words **implied**. It was just another way of saying "You disgust me, moron," but politely.

Billy **meandered** out the door, spitting against the outside wall as he headed towards the cafeteria, where teriyaki hotdogs were the menu. "You're safe in the streets," he reminded himself. Safe from the confinement of school, parents and from his inner **malaise**, a feeling which **gnawed** within him and demanded an answer. What was he doing right now in school, in his life? Where was he going? His **boundless** imagination leaped **chimerically** in all directions, to faraway places where *Ferraris* and blonde blue-eyed girls **lingered**, where **intemperate** revelry was in **vogue**, where life was just one big video game and he was a *Super Mario Brother* **surmounting** all the obstacles, victorious over all new worlds which challenged him. He could be the **invincible**, the **Sugar Ray Leonard** of the '90s. It was all just waiting for him to enter and experience. "You're safe in the streets." Butch must have known what he was saying – it sounded so appealing.

"Hey, Spit, what're you doin' here?" Billy looked up and viewed his **dreaded nemesis**. The boy was bigger than he was, eighty pounds bigger. Sam Herman never liked him, not since Billy had **intimated** to friends that Sam was gay. It was just a **jocose insinuation**, but the school and Sam never forgot it. A year had passed, and Billy had managed to either avoid Sam or simply slip away. But the two would eventually cross paths again, and the time had come.

"Hi, Sam. Long time no see," the **diminutive** lad squeaked **mousily**. Billy **longed** to be on the streets rather than in front of Sam the brute. He attempted to **saunter** casually by, but Sam's words were not to be ignored.

"I haven't forgotten you, you little runt. If this wasn't school, you'd be on your knees. I'm telling you this now, punk. You watch where you walk. 'Cause one day, you're gonna meet me somewhere else, and I'll show you what pain is. Your time's coming soon, you can bet on it." The muscular jock took a deep breath, then turned and walked away in a slow and **deliberate** pace, all the while appearing as though prepared to turn around and spring on his **prey** at any given moment. But his

"I haven't forgotten you, you little runt."

strong-willed self-containment kept his temper in **check**. Nonetheless, his threat was serious, and Billy knew that his most feared enemy had finally **illuminated** him to future events he dared not dwell on since the seventh-grade incident first occurred.

Billy **endeavored** to respond, to either say something to protect his fragile **ego** or else attempt to **propitiate** the **virile** warrior. But nothing came out. The words were not there. Somehow they weren't meant to come out. Whatever lay in the future could not be changed, and Billy momentarily **pondered** the possibilities. No matter what, the future seemed more exciting than the past. There were so many options, so many ideas to consider, so many possible new worlds about to open up for him. Even the feeling of pain seemed attractive. Anything was better than the dull routine of school, the stale threats of his folks and the **desultory** direction that **stifled** his efforts to **manumit** himself and journey **unshackled** to meet his **destiny**.

The lunch bell interrupted his brief **introspective digression**, from which Billy emerged with renewed **vigor** and **animation**. There was much to look forward to. And it all was waiting out there in the streets, where the real people lived.

CHAPTER IV
Setting The Stage

"Billy, I was hoping you'd be here." Billy Steele turned to see Jeanine, his long-time girlfriend, walking towards him carrying a math book under her right arm. "Did you finish your homework for today?"

"No, Jenny, I really didn't. Why?"

"Oh, I just thought you could help me with the last problem. I got two different answers, and now I'm not sure which is right."

"Maybe they're both right," Billy **quipped**, **employing** his **quirky relativistic rationale**.

"Billy, what happened with you in Costello's class? I heard you got thrown out. Someone said you tried to hit her."

"Sure, Jenny," he answered in **jest**, "but I missed and ran to Stimson's office and hit him instead. Then I beat up Sam Herman and now I'm hungry because I beat up so many people."

"All right, I can take a hint. I won't mention any more of it, okay?" Jenny smiled and tilted her head, gazing at Billy as if trying to **coax** a mynah bird to say a few words.

"So, what're you looking at now, Juliet?"

"Just another Romeo, I guess. You sure are cute when you're not talking, you know that?" She always had a way of making Billy blush, a feeling that he loved except when other students were around. She really was a spark of magic for him, a friend whose presence grew from puppy love to an odd form of **kinship**. She had always found a way to open him up, to make him reveal his warmth and humanity, in a way no one else could ever do. She was one of those rare girl friends who accepted him as he was, with all his faults and all his blessings. And she also reminded him of the many **attributes** he possessed.

"Jenny, I'm thinking of digging out."

"Digging out?" she echoed. "What do you mean? From what?"

"From school, from my folks, from everything. Just packing it up and hitting the streets."

"Why? What's so bad about school, and you've got a nice home, too." Jenny's attention was firmly focused as she listened for the response.

"Nothing's bad, but it's all really screwed up. There's just no way out unless I 'bag'. I'm stuck here and I'll always be stuck here. I can't move, I can't find myself, I can't see the world. I'm just **stagnating** here on this rock, in this school. I need to grow up." He stared out toward the horizon, to the streets that lay beyond the walls of the school. "I'm safe in the streets, Jenny. I think I can find myself there."

Jenny was hushed. It was so unexpected, her favorite boyfriend suddenly talking as though he were an adult dissatisfied with his many years of struggle. The display just didn't **befit** a thirteen-year-old boy who didn't even know how to wash his own clothes, least of all be able to **fend** for himself in a wild, dangerous world filled with **sinister** people she wouldn't even dare to think of **encountering** alone.

"Why?" she finally found herself asking.

"Because it's there!" Billy screamed **frenetically** and **adamantly**. "Because I want to. Because it's my life. Oh, so many reasons, Jenny. I can't even begin to tell you. It's where the answers to life's secrets lie. It's all out there in the streets. 'Tell them that it's human nature,' I guess."

Michael Jackson's words weren't convincing to Jenny. The decision was just too **rash**, too unplanned, too **juvenile**. But it was not to be taken lightly, either. Billy's **impetuous whims** could never be dismissed. Jenny had learned to accept that ever since the day Billy had said he'd climb to the top of the roof of Ordman Hall, towering forty feet above the cement courtyard. With his **penchant** for **melodrama**, he did it right in the middle of the lunch recess, stepping one foot off the **protruding** ledge while Jenny, Stewart and others watched in **mute** horror. He had won $5 from the dare, and Butch Van Moren never again challenged the **intrepidly foolhardy** lad to do anything that was humanly possible. The **graphic** display clearly demonstrated that Billy would try anything.

"If you gotta go, please be careful. You know where you can reach me, Billy. I'll always be there."

"Thanks, Jenny, you're a true friend," and then he leaned over and kissed her on her closed lips. She shrank back in amazement, **bemused** and **befuddled** from the first physical contact the two had ever made. The timing of his affection made her feel uncomfortable, as though it were a farewell kiss. The image of Romeo and Juliet was too alive now to act dreamily. A shudder of fear penetrated her body, and she sought to fight back as best she could.

"Please be careful, Billy," she **entreated**. "Please be careful."

"Don't worry, Jen, the streets are safe," he added for **reassurance** as they parted company. His mind wandering once more, Billy drifted both in body and spirit to the cafeteria and the inviting flavor of the **sapid** teriyaki morsels.

Stewart was already seated with a couple of friends, eating his cole slaw and guzzling down the chocolate milk, when Billy arrived. "Finally made it, huh Snick?" he gasped between gulps.

"Yeah, Stew, I'm here. Like they say, 'Here today, gone to Maui.'"

"What does that mean?" Stewart asked as he slowed down his pace of eating and drinking. "Oh I see, you're still heading out?" he added, sensing Billy's single-mindedness to **extricate** himself from his perceived **circumscription** and blaze a new trail.

"Yeah, I'm going out tonight. Coming with me, Stew?"

The invitation was informal but serious. Billy was going with or without his best friend, and Stewart was ready for the question. "No, but I'll be around when you need me," he said with **staid solemnity**. "You know I'll help you any way you want. Understand me?"

The others didn't grasp the **gist** of the conversation, so there was no need to explain anything.

"Sure, Stew, you'll know where I am. I just wanted to be sure I asked you, that's all. Just between friends."

The group shared in their lunch, nothing more said about his **visionary** ideas. Billy had let everyone important know, and now he felt comfortable that he had the support group he needed in case his plans went **awry** or failed to reach **fruition**. Stew knew, Jenny knew, and Butch knew. Billy was now ready to enter the real world and see life from the other side.

School had never before felt so uncomplicated, so unattached and **unencumbering**, as it did for Billy that afternoon. Nothing could affect him or his **utopian** plans. Mrs. Valenzuela didn't need to remind him to settle down, and even Stewart couldn't get his attention. His thoughts were **riveted** on the **inscrutable destiny** that welcomed his arrival, a future **replete** with **hitherto** unexplored avenues assuring adventures unparalleled in the **annals** of recorded history. Billy was indeed eager to **embark** upon his **picaresque peregrination**.

For the adventurous adolescent, the exit would represent the third time he'd run away but the first that would surely be successful. When he had fled in the sixth grade, he had no idea where he was going or even why he was running. It all happened over a misunderstanding, something about not eating dinner. He couldn't really remember the circumstances, and even when he walked out the door at 8:00 p.m., he didn't know why he was leaving.

In the seventh grade, his departure had more significance. He had quarreled with his parents over his allowance, arguing that he couldn't do anything on $10 per week. He had a more **substantial** basis for his argument, concluding that there were better opportunities in the outside world to survive. The idea was sound, but his determination wasn't firm. In the sixth grade, his parents had gone out and found him walking around; in the seventh grade, he returned two hours later without any **fanfare** – Billy's parents were not even aware of his absence.

But this year, things were different. The pressures to **conform** to school codes, family rules and **mundane** regulations **rankled** within and **engendered** an **enmity** for authoritarian **directives** and an **aversion** to the **status quo**. His imagination had developed and **flourished** since the seventh grade, and he now saw himself compromising his own **integrity** by **abiding** the **mediocrity** and restrictiveness of his home life and **submitting** to a life of **unremitting ennui**.

All Billy had needed was a **cue**, an **impetus** to **induce** him to take the plunge, a silent dare to **kindle** the passion to prove his self-worth and risk his **meager** existence with the hope of discovering an **Elysian** paradise beyond the **prosaic circumscription** of an **otiose subsistence**. *Lady M* had indeed delivered that **seductive** dare, her **sensuously** rosy pink lips **exhorting** him to escape into the world of the unknown, where everything that awaited would be fresh, alive, and daringly attractive. "Two hearts that beat as one..." would be his guiding inspiration, his **shibboleth impelling** him to pursue his dreams. The words could fuel his imagination whenever he might feel the dream **waning**.

Billy had **dwelt** on the words for hours, projecting himself into the street-scene and **pondering** all the **sundry scenarios**. The worst that might **befall** him would be tough times, no friends, and always the fear of the police looking for him. But the best far outweighed the worst, for he would find freedom, meet new friends and visit new places. He would be the master of his own **destiny**, something he could never **envision** in his present lifestyle. And if he were to have second thoughts, he would merely need to hear *Lady M*'s words pounding against his own heart and he'd know that a hidden treasure might await him around the next corner, or a new opportunity for **salvation proffered** by the next person he might **encounter**.

"Billy Steele, are you sleeping?" Mrs. Valenzuela **interposed**, disrupting his **tranquil** train of thought.

"No Ma'am. I'm still here."

Stewart mumbled a few words in his general direction, obviously the answer to a question the teacher had just asked.

"Since you're not listening to me, maybe you ought to go out into the hall until you regain your sense of hearing." The veteran teacher then pointed out towards the hall, and Billy reluctantly grabbed his small bundle of books and prepared to take the long, embarrassing **trek** through the classroom, past the **jeering** from all his **peers** – friend and **foe** alike – and out into the corridor. **Barbs**, chuckles and **innuendos** came from all directions, from everyone. Everyone except Stew. He would always stick by Billy, through thick and thin.

"Leave those books, young man. You are planning on returning, I hope?" Mrs. Valenzuela asked with **facetious derision**.

Billy stopped for a moment as he was about to exit the room, then turned and added in a matter-of-fact tone, "No, I don't think so. I'll just take my books. Thanks anyway." He then **ambled blithely** out through the doorway while the class sat speechless, awed by his unexpectedly **jaunty demeanor**. Rather than **eliciting** ridicule, Billy had generated envy from the students, many of whom secretly may have wished to follow him to freedom. He had produced a silent revolution, but he knew he wouldn't let anyone know how far he was going. No one but Stewart.

As he left the classroom, he continued to walk on, out of the history building, out to the track, then across the field in the direction of the bus stop. He wasn't stopping now. The journey had begun. He hesitated as he reached the bus stop and looked up at the clear, cloudless sky, the **scintillating** sunshine blazing down eighty-five degrees of April warmth in the land where the sun never says goodbye. He knew he wouldn't leave the island, not unless his pursuit for freedom would be **jeopardized**. He could manage to find places to stay in Hawaii. After all, there were **ample** video game parlors and shopping malls, not to mention a **bevy** of **beneficent** babes eager to assist a young boy in his search for shelter. There wasn't much to worry about. The future had now become a thrilling and **boundless** avenue **auguring auspicious** opportunities, and as he looked up at the sky he felt his life beginning anew. He would now be Mr. Billy Steele, his own boss, following his own dreams and fighting his own battles. He wouldn't need his parents to shelter him anymore; he was ready to prove that he could fulfill his most **aspiring** ambitions by himself.

The bus rolled up, and Billy stepped through the opened door, ready to travel ahead in time. The next stop: Waikiki.

He had produced a silent revolution, but he knew he wouldn't let anyone know how far he was going.

CHAPTER V
The Helping Hand

"Kind of early for you to be out of school, huh sonny?" the old man sitting next to him said in casual conversation. The young **waif** looked up at the stranger, detecting a **probing** seriousness about him, as though the senior citizen had experienced the same childhood and knew what the runaway was planning to do. Or was it just Billy's imagination, his **perception** that everyone was eyeing him and witnessing his escape? Could he even get away with his bold escape amid a **multitude** of eyes watching his every move? Billy looked about, but no one was looking back. He was safe. Alone but safe. Butch was right – the streets were safe. Alone but safe.

"No, mister," he replied at last, "I'm just headed to visit some relatives...That's all."

The old man didn't reply; his words were meant only to break the silence, nothing more. He got up to exit at the next bus stop, and Billy was left unbothered. The outside world was beginning to make itself more clear to him. Nobody else cared, not like his parents did. He wasn't accountable to anyone here, and the new-found freedom made his senses swirl as though he had experienced a rush from a **stimulant**, the way he felt last week when he and Stewart had found a bottle of cement glue and sniffed the remaining contents. The **fugitive** moment produced an **intoxicating exhilaration** for the duo, similar to the **euphoric** sensation that now **animated** his thoughts. No longer merely a passenger on a bus, he visualized himself riding in a limousine headed to Hollywood. He was going to be a star, and the world would soon discover Billy Steele, rock-idol of the '90s. The image pulsated in his brain, and he stuck out his chest **vaingloriously** as though living the part of the ***Don Juan*** of Honolulu. He felt proud, and the world looked exciting.

"Next stop, Waikiki," the driver echoed **perfunctorily** to the half-crowded bus. Tourists scrambled hastily from their seats, Billy following **nonchalantly** behind to exit last. Last but not least. The silent star. His imagination raced wildly as he observed Waikiki as never before. It was no longer just a weekend **haunt**. It was a new beginning, a new world, a new and **embryonic** challenge. All the places he'd seen before would become his new home, and all the exotic spots would be new adventures. There were enough places to **divert** and **engage** him for the rest of his life.

"Well, Snick, you've arrived," he told himself with **smug** satisfaction. "Take a good look, 'cause you've made it." The words started out as a whisper but ended in a voice that attracted stares from nearby tourists.

"Is this your first time in Waikiki?" a young lady asked him as she overheard the final words.

"Yes, ma'm, sure is."

"Well, I'm sure you'll like it. I've been here for three weeks."

"I'm sure I'll like it after I'm here three weeks, ma'm." He **snickered** to himself, conscious of the nickname that **aptly** labeled his **idiosyncratic mannerism**. He loved to **dabble** with **double entendre**, words that **denoted** more than anyone else ever suspected. His very nickname held a deeper glimpse into his character. Others knew he liked to eat Snickers candy bars, but the nickname carried a more personal meaning, known only to Billy himself. 'Snicker' was more than a nickname; it reflected an attitude toward his very existence. For the young traveler, life was but an **evanescent** dream to observe and make sport of, and all the people merely **pawns** to be **manipulated**. Snickering at others' **follies** as if to say "That's not my concern," Billy maintained a separate and **detached** identity as though a **transient** onlooker personally unaffected by anything others did or said. But when he desired center-stage, all he needed to do was wriggle his nose and pop his tongue against one cheek, and **unwitting** grown-ups would be at his **beck** and call. The teachers didn't fall for his **guise** of innocence, but his parents did and so did most adults he met. To them he was the ideal young man, **ingratiatingly** courteous and desirous of adult **approbation**. But in **sooth**, Billy sought freedom and power – freedom to move without restrictions and power to have others follow him. The lady tourist was his latest victim. And as he could charm her into believing him, so too could the **wily rapscallion** get anything he wanted simply by **cavalierly wheedling** and **inveigling** the ignorant masses through a **callow guise** of **vernal artlessness**.

The radiant afternoon sun beat down upon him as he headed for the *Waikiki Video Factory*. Although **clad** in long pants and a blue-and-white cotton shirt, Billy had taken along his gym shorts and a cut-off t-shirt. His duffel bag also contained some other assorted clothes, packed in the event he might choose to head out to the beach after school. He had a towel, slippers and a ten-dollar bill. A few other **auxiliary** odds-and-ends were scattered throughout the bag, including a pocket knife and some dental floss, but what he had was **sufficient** for Waikiki. What he didn't bring, he could purchase or **cajole** a kindhearted **altruistic** vacationer into purchasing for him. And if all else failed, he could always **purloin** the product. There was no **dearth** of retail stores in the neighborhood, so finding what he wanted and **appropriating** it posed no real problem. He had long mastered the art of **pilfering**, knowing the best places and best times to **effectuate** his **artifice**. Whether for candy bars or sunglasses, Billy knew the most **efficient** way to get what he wanted. He learned by other people's mistakes and thereby avoided falling victim to the **surveillance** traps and other forms of preventive detection **prevalent** throughout the retail industry. Billy Steele knew that he could outsmart the most **sophisticated** technological devices – he'd never been caught before – and he was sure he could **fend** for himself even under the most **trying** of circumstances.

One issue was of **paramount** concern, however: Billy would need to avoid the police, especially after the **curfew** hour of 10:00 p.m. His parents would certainly begin to look for him almost immediately, and though they wouldn't suspect his precise whereabouts the police would surely check Waikiki in search of him. In the meanwhile, the young explorer had at least five or six hours to secure a safe **haven** for the long evening.

His feet took him swiftly to the *Waikiki Video Factory*, **inconspicuously** entering a dark room filled with flashing lights and **dulcet** sounds. The games whirled and **gyrated**, **employing** a variety of **savory** sights and **euphonious** melodies intended to **entice** passersby to drop a quarter into the slot and **engage** in alien battle against another dimension. Some machines **whirred**, others actually spoke words, while still others produced a hypnotic **mellifluence**. They all combined to produce an **aura** of dreamland, a world where nothing was real except that which the imagination chose to follow. This was Billy's world, his **emancipation** from the **execrable** artistic **suppression espoused** by a **wizened aristocracy**.

Alone and at peace to evaluate his own direction, the **fledgling** voyager plotted his next move. With **ample** time but limited resources, he knew the best approach to remain undetected would be to play only those video games he had mastered in the past. He needed to remain occupied by **frugally** getting the most out of every quarter, at least until he had **procured** a dependable flow of income.

A couple of hours passed by as Billy clung tight to *Super Mario Brothers*, then shifting his attention and **protracting** his stay by another ninety minutes with one quarter against *Pac Man*. His stomach growled as the evening hours drew **nigh**, but his concentration in the game overpowered his urge for **sustenance**. The newest edition of *Pac Man* became the sole focus of his efforts as he sat **entranced** before it, and when the game was finally over Billy glanced to his side to see the afternoon now **veiled** in black. It was a few minutes past nine o'clock, and his hunger returned with an **irrepressible vengeance**.

"Hi, kid," a voice from behind **wafted** through the temporary stillness. The **timbre** wasn't familiar, the words weren't familiar, and he wasn't addressed by name, but Billy knew the words were meant for him. His immediate reaction would normally have been to turn and acknowledge the stranger, but he knew only too well that the police were now looking for him, that this could be the end of his short-lived dream.

The voice didn't repeat itself, and Billy edged around cautiously to see if the person was still there.

"Like I said, hi." It was not a cop. The man appeared too casual to be a cop. He wore white tennis shorts, a red pullover shirt and *Nike* jogging shoes. If he were a policeman, he wasn't dressed like one.

Billy realized that he had no choice but to reply. He couldn't survive in the wild if he was afraid of everyone who spoke to him, so he offered the next words. "Hi, how're you doin'?"

"I'm doin' fine, kid. Couldn't help but notice you doing a number on that game, though. What did you score? A million?"

Billy's pride was aroused. "Well, not really. I scored two million. Almost."

"Wow. You were on that game for over an hour, and I watched most of it. You live around

"Hi, kid," a voice from behind him wafted through the temporary stillness.

here?"

"Uh, well, kind of. You see, I'm visiting my dad. My folks are **divorced**, and I'm here for a couple weeks." The story came out smoothly, but he couldn't tell whether his facts were believable.

"I see, so you're gonna be around for a while still, huh?"

Billy **contemplated** the words carefully. The man wasn't an undercover policeman or else he wouldn't have added the last words. He might simply be another tourist, just what Billy needed.

"Yeah, I'm just hanging around," Billy added, more confidently. "You see, my dad doesn't really care where I go, so I'm just hanging around here by myself and enjoying the two weeks, before I go back to... uh...Dallas."

"Well, you sure don't have a Texan accent, son...but then again, you're only a kid, so that's not unusual."

Billy started to add a few words with the best Southwestern drawl he could **muster**, but as the words left his mouth they fell flat. He couldn't fake a Texan accent and the older gentleman hadn't questioned it at length, so Billy just let the matter drop. "No, I guess I just never picked it up. I used to live in California and Ohio, so I don't think I really ever got any accent."

"That makes sense," the man added. "And I can imagine that you're a bit hungry, too, huh?"

The words reminded Billy's stomach to start complaining, and even within the noisiness of the video games his stomach managed to **bellow** a loud, deep growl which he felt couldn't have been missed by anyone within a hundred yards. "Yeah, I'm starved," he replied in a matter-of-fact way. "I could use a good meal."

"Well, how about we treat ourselves to Waikiki and share a meal together? My name's Lenny, by the way."

"Oh, my name's..." Should he be Billy or Steve or Sam or Stewart or John or Jim? His imagination was racing without end and, before he could decide, the older friend added "Any name is fine, son. I don't want to put you on the spot."

The kindness from the man, the **unqualified** acceptance of whatever Billy wanted to say left a strange impression on the boy. He could use any name he wanted, but all of a sudden he didn't feel the need to hide his true self. "I'm 'Snicker'. That's my nickname, and I like it a lot. So you can call me 'Snicker,' okay?"

"Sure, Snicker. I like that name, too. It's got real character. I think you're a special young man. Can't see why your father wouldn't pay more attention to you."

"Oh, that's okay. I just want to see Waikiki by myself. He's really a cool guy. But you know how it is. I'm thirteen years old and I want to be on my own." The words came out so quickly, so freely that Billy stopped suddenly to see what impression it had on Lenny.

"Well, I'm convinced. Let's hit the town. Waikiki awaits, and we can always talk over a steak, right?"

"Steak? Sounds right dandy to me," Billy concluded in whatever Texan **jargon** he could create. He had eaten steak at home, but now that he was on his own he knew a **succulent** steak would be as rare a word as 'money,' and he **relished** the invitation as never before. Nothing could be taken for granted anymore, and the thrill of the challenge of survival sent shivers through his body. Not even one day had passed, yet he was experiencing the excitement of everyday existence with a renewed **verve** and **ardor** he thought had been **usurped** by years of artistic imprisonment and **deprivation**. Free at last, Billy saw Lenny **literally** as his 'meal-ticket,' an expression that assumed added significance now that he was living on the streets.

"Let's go," Billy added eagerly, grabbing his duffel bag. The two strolled out of the video parlor and soon into the world of dining, Billy safe alongside his **eleemosynary** escort. Everything was going just perfectly.

"Table for two?" the **maitre d'** at the *Waikiki Nightcomber* asked politely though **indifferently** as the two entered the beachside hotel restaurant.

"Yes, for me and my son," Lenny responded proudly.

But the words weren't well received by Billy. "I've already got a father," he thought to himself. "That's what I'm getting away from. The last thing I need is another person trying to act like my parent." The man's words **embedded** themselves in his innermost soul.

"Well, Snicker, how does Waikiki look so far?"

"Yeah, it's nice," came the immediate response. But the thoughts behind the reply spoke differently, echoing deep within him a **cautionary** unpleasance: "Is he trying to **impress** me with his money? I don't need someone else to try to buy my companionship." The mood of the evening was changing rapidly. The **euphoria** of the escape was now assuming a more **sinister semblance**, that of a **precarious predicament** with potentially **perilous repercussions**. He was gripped by an uncertainty bordering between **trepidation** and outright fear.

The two were seated and soon ready to order, but Billy's appetite quickly disappeared when Lenny's big, wide hands reached out to surround him in a **camaraderie** far too **premature** and **presumptuous** to encourage friendship. Lenny was either a lonely tourist looking for an island **amigo** or else he was seeking some cheap thrills. Billy wasn't about to find out which.

The two were seated and soon ready to order...

"Uh, can you excuse me for a moment...Lenny?" He had almost forgotten the man's name amid the confusion and panic that swept over him. "I need to go to..." But his words fell short. He didn't even want to make any references which might **stimulate** further problems. Lenny didn't answer, waiting instead for Billy to continue the sentence.

· The young man moved away nervously but impatiently, bowing in some out-of-place gesture of courtesy, knowing full-well that he might just as likely have **bolted** out the front door instead.

The **engagement** was over and Billy found himself quickly back on the street, hurrying to another video parlor, as far away from the restaurant and the *Video Factory* as his feet could carry him. His senses were spinning; he was in a cross-current going nowhere, avoiding the police, avoiding the man with the big hands, and yet looking for somewhere to turn, somewhere to find **refuge**.

It was after 10:00 p.m. – the local **curfew** hour – and Billy knew the police were most certainly now alerted that he was a runaway. Should he call his folks? Was it time to quit and go home? Or would the police end his **lark** and bring him back in handcuffs? As he walked towards an unknown resting place, the **famished** blond-haired **fledgling** slowed his pace, bowed his head down – covering his face with his hands – and wept lightly.

"Hey, watch where you're going," one **surly** passerby **scowled** as the two bumped each other on the crowded sidewalk. But the young **waif** kept on walking, peeking out **periodically** from behind his covered face to follow the **cacophonous** flow of **pedestrian** traffic.

The next voice he heard sounded more official, and as he gazed upwards Billy stared directly at a policeman holding a nightstick. "Having problems, son?" the officer asked in a concerned tone.

"No sir," Billy added in a cracked voice. "Just walking home."

"Where do you live, son?"

"Uh...I'm on vacation, sir. Just going home, sir, that's all." The defense strategy was weak, but his entire shortened experience wasn't turning out as he had predicted, his creative inventiveness giving way to the **grim** reality of his situation. He had no place to go and he couldn't find an answer, real or imaginary, to present to the officer.

"Where are you staying, son?" the man continued. "I can take you there. No problem." The end seemed near.

"Oh there you are, Johnny," a soft voice in the background interrupted. "I've been looking all over for you."

The policeman turned with Billy to see a young woman in her late twenties smiling nervously at the two.

27

"I've been looking all over for you."

"I'm sorry, officer, I guess he just got lost. I'll take you home right now." With those final words, she grabbed Billy's hand and dragged him along in the direction of the *Video Factory* and the man with the big hands, back into the heart of Waikiki.

"Well, ma'm, you should look out a little more for your son, you know that," the policeman yelled somewhat angrily. "This place isn't safe for teenagers after dark." He obviously didn't suspect that Billy was a runaway, and the lady had now offered the perfect **alibi** to **safeguard** Billy's freedom awhile longer.

"Keep moving, Johnny," the lady whispered as the two walked swiftly away from the policeman, who continued his regular rounds without further interference.

"Thanks, lady, but my name's Billy, not Johnny."

"Oh, I don't care," she replied impatiently. "Let's just get out of here before that stupid pig comes after us."

Billy observed his latest **savior** as they walked quickly, holding hands as though fleeing a fire. She was rather pretty, with dark blonde hair, long fingernails which cut into his wrists and a **skimpy** tight pink skirt with white high-heel shoes. Over her shoulder hung a small pink purse, giving the impression that she was dressed specially for the occasion. Everything matched, as though she had not accidentally gone to Waikiki.

"Are you a hooker?" Billy asked without **reserve**. He wasn't ashamed to ask the question. It was just a matter-of-fact **query**.

"Honey, right now I'm just trying to save your ever-lovin' ass." Her reply was **frank** and honest, and Billy understood her **tacit** response to his **blatant** question. She was.

The two turned away from the crowd and into a **secluded** side-street, coming upon a thirty-story high-rise, one of the dozens which towered over Waikiki and cast evening shadows even in the heat of the afternoon sun. The lady unlocked the front gate and the two entered the hotel lobby, a **stark** and **austere** room which led to two elevators. The hotel was large but not glamorous, and yet it represented for Billy a much-appreciated escape from the world outside. He was safe, or at least as safe as the lady was. Thoughts of the man with the big hands created a sudden **quiver** throughout his entire body. He had escaped from one problem and was now hostage in a lobby with a woman he had never before met. He was becoming more entrapped with every move.

"Ma'm, I think I better leave. Thanks for your help."

But her reply **reassured** him and left him in a **placid** state of contentment. "Honey, relax. I'm not going to hurt you. I can spot a runaway a mile away. I was one myself. I just don't want to see you get hurt. Okay?"

The elevator arrived and carried them up to the fourteenth floor, which led in both directions to what seemed an endless **array** of hotel rooms.

"Listen honey, you stay here," the lady said as she entered the room closest to the elevator. After a few seconds, she returned. "Okay, you can come on in – it's my room. You're safe here. And here's the key."

Billy entered as she handed him the key to room 1426. The hotel room was a one-bedroom complex, small but elegantly **adorned** with **plush** red quilt carpeting, a color television, an **elaborate** bathroom complete with a full-size bath, and a view overlooking the mountainside, facing away from Waikiki.

"I think you'll like it here, honey. Just stay here and make yourself comfortable. There's some cereal in the 'fridge."

Billy was at a loss for words. Within ten minutes, he was snatched from the clutches of the police and now had possession of the keys to his own hotel room. "Thanks, ma'm," he finally **uttered**, **incredulously**.

But the young woman was already on her way out to the elevator and didn't hear his **timid gratitude**. "I'll be back in a while. Just keep the door locked and don't open it except for me, understand?"

Billy nodded, and the lady looked back at him and smiled. "You're cute, Johnny, real cute," and then she slipped into the elevator and was gone.

CHAPTER VI
The Intruder

The evening moon shone through the large glass sliding doors, inviting Billy to open them and walk through to view the **panoramic vista** from the balcony. Gazing towards the neighboring structures, Billy mentally replayed the events which had brought him here. His **wanderlust** had all developed from a **whim**, a **fancy** to take to the streets and explore a lifestyle **untrammeled** by parents, school or anything **constrictive**. But now he had a moment to **ruminate** on the events, and his thoughts drifted back to his home. His parents were probably still awake, **fretting** and **speculating** why he wanted to leave or whether he did indeed leave of his own **accord**. His home wasn't really so bad, but he couldn't convince his parents that he could care for himself. They always placed restrictions why he couldn't go out, couldn't sleep over at a friend's house, or couldn't watch a specific movie. The household was filled with 'don'ts,' but Billy's **fecund** imagination **goaded** him to pursue an **unhindered** path rather than **capitulate** to a life **circumscribed** by **stipulations** and **mandated subservience**.

Billy then turned this thoughts to Stewart, his closest friend, and what Stewart must have been thinking tonight. Did Billy's parents call him? And if they did, would he tell them anything? But what did he himself know? Nothing except that Billy wanted to run away. Nothing more than that. No destination, no plans, no real direction, just simply 'running away' as young kids threaten to do when all they really want is attention. But was this plan **executed** for attention or was this a genuine and realistic pursuit for freedom? Billy **pensively pondered** his **perplexing predicament** as he looked down into the dark, **desolate** and dangerous back-streets of Waikīkī. He was safe fourteen stories above it all, but he knew he would be returning to the streets sooner or later. He couldn't live the rest of his life on the fourteenth floor.

Focusing on the bright side of his recent developments, Billy had broken free from his parents, had made a close friendship with a woman who offered him shelter, and now had the opportunity to decide for himself what to do next. This was a **vast** improvement over his home life, where all the decisions were determined by his overprotective caretakers. He was now free to discover his own **destiny**.

The teenage explorer turned on the television and viewed a cable-TV movie, an old classic restored by colorization. He sprawled **supine** upon the extra-firm single-bed, looking up at the screen which lay mounted on the opposite wall, puzzling over how to satisfy his next immediate need. As *Humphrey Bogart* sat in a restaurant eyeing what everyone else was having for dinner, Billy's stomach reminded him that his own hunger had not yet been **appeased**. In his moment of relaxed **deliberation**, the **vagabond** youngster tugged on his shirt and combed back his hair, paying particular attention to his shoulder-length tail which draped from the middle of the back of his neck, a **queue** which had taken him fully a year to **nurture** to full length. He was proud of this physical uniqueness, the only symbol of individuality which his parents hadn't controlled. Despite their efforts, he wouldn't cut the tail. They finally **resigned** themselves to getting used to it, at least until

Billy mentally replayed the events which had brought him here.

their son would, as they told him, "stop being a baby and learn to grow up." But here he was, growing up quickly, and yet his proud possession was in no **peril**.

With his hair straightened out and his body stretched comfortably across the bed, Billy now addressed his appetite. He climbed slowly off the bed and rolled onto the floor in a lazy, slow motion, eventually picking himself up off the richly soft carpeting and walking wearily to the small refrigerator that lay under the wet-bar.

"Yeah," he exclaimed excitedly to himself as the door opened to reveal *Frosted Flakes*, his favorite, and a full quart of milk. All he needed was a spoon and bowl and he would be set for the evening.

In no time he found his utensils and hurriedly prepared a meal fit for a king – or more fitting, for a prince, a young **regal** warrior. *Bogart* looked down at him as Billy **ravenously** tore into the **prey**, making sounds like a tiger in the process. "Sorry, mister, this is mine. All mine." Even *Bogey* couldn't take it away from him.

The first and second bowls emptied themselves in quick succession, but the third went more slowly. Having satisfied his **primary craving**, Billy was getting tired. The activities of the day and the energy **expended** in the moments of fear and doubt had left him unusually **fatigued**; he now felt the full impact of the strain. The **languid** lad struggled to return the milk to the refrigerator and then plopped onto the bed. Amid all the confusion, the young **stray** had somewhere misplaced his duffel bag and now sensed that he had **literally** only the clothes on him, nothing more. But that was another problem for another time; right now, all he wanted was to rest so he could face tomorrow energized and **revitalized**. As *Bogey* recited some memorable lines, Billy Steele went off into his own fantasyland, departing from his self-exile and returning home in his dreams.

The **indispensable interlude** was short-lived, however. A **resonating** bang brought the tired traveler back from his own **ethereal** escape to a world **vaguely** familiar, yet uninvitingly **sterile**. The knocking persisted, and he knew at once someone wanted to enter the apartment. The bedside clock indicated 2:30 a.m., only a few short hours after he'd first fallen asleep. His **cranium** began to throb and pulse, and his stomach felt **uneasy**. He jerked his head up but his body refused to follow, and he fell in a slump back onto the bed.

After an all-too-brief pause, the **stentorian resonance** resumed. Someone was **intent** on entering, and Billy couldn't avoid the banging no matter how hard he tried to shut it out.

"Yeah, hold on…" he said drowsily. "Give me a minute, okay?"

He staggered from atop the bed and **endeavored** to lift his head to see who was waiting outside. But in his **somnolent** state, his head remained bowed while his body **wavered** from side to side, trying to keep balance. As he reached the door, he leaned against it and dozed off again for a brief moment. Then the pounding erupted, his body instantly perking up and his eyes **jolting** open as though he were injected with a shot of caffeine.

He poked one eye into the peep-hole to see who was waiting, but there was no one outside. He looked more closely, staring down at the floor, then to the left, then to the right. Someone was waiting, but the person was crouched to the side of the door, and all Billy could make out was a dark shadow.

"Who's there?" he echoed with more volume. "I can't let you in if I don't know who you are." He tried to recall what the lady had said. Did she say not to let anyone in, or did she say something else? In his **slumberous** state Billy could not get his thoughts together, so he awaited instead for some reply to help him decide what to do.

"I'm the wolf, you little punk, and you're in my house." The words weren't offered in **jest**; the person was unmistakably serious about every word he said. Billy tried to revive himself to a **sober** state in order to **assess** the situation, but his thirteen-year-old body wasn't used to the short sleep and loud banging, and his thoughts couldn't piece themselves together.

The **invasive** intruder continued in his **malevolent timbre**. "And if you don't open that door, I'll break it down. So open it. Now."

There wasn't much else to do. Maybe it *was* his room. Maybe the lady had found the keys, or borrowed the keys, or even stolen the keys.

"I'm sorry, mister, I didn't know it's your place." Although he tried to sound convincing, Billy couldn't come out from his **soporific** state to fully comprehend or answer to the **gravity** of the situation. His words were almost **monotone**.

"Look, kid, my woman told me you'd be here, so just open the door, okay. I've got a key, but you've got the deadbolt locked. So unlock the latch, that's all. Then you can go back to sleep." The man perceived the lad's drowsy condition and had said the right words to make Billy feel comfortable and safe.

The bolt was unlatched, and Billy could then hear the key in the lock. The man really did have the keys. The place was his, after all.

The door opened with force and Billy fell backwards, landing helplessly back upon the bed. The man stood there, all two hundred solid pounds of muscle, a **swarthy** man who sported white shorts and a tanktop which **accentuated** his **brawny** physical **contour**. His hair was braided and he wore a gold chain around his neck. Billy realized that he was a man of both physical and financial **prominence**.

"Suzy said you were cute, and I guess she was right," he began in a more **soothingly subdued**

34

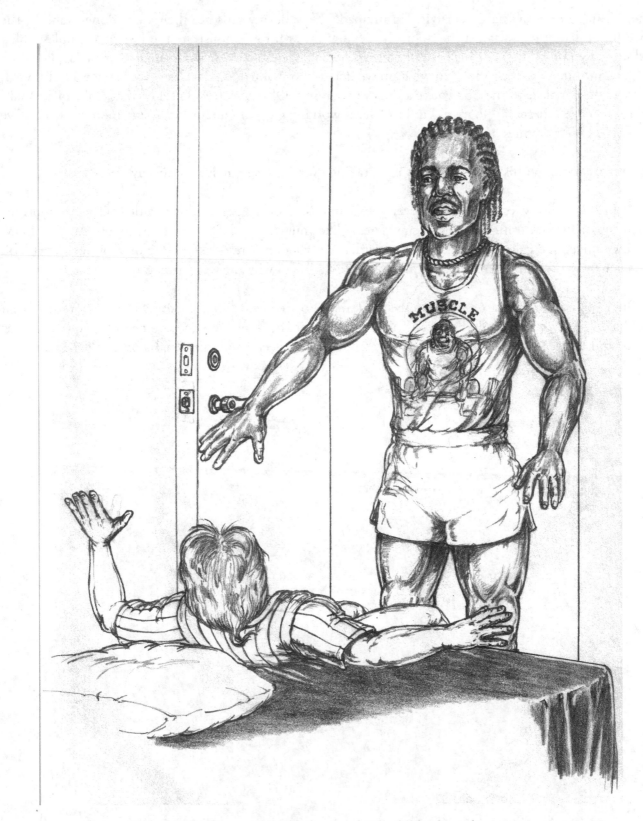

The door opened with force and Billy fell backwards...

tone. "But son, I can't have you living in my pad. How do my girls get their work done, huh?" The powerful athlete leaned against the doorway, **flexing** one arm to demonstrate the muscular ripples which undoubtedly ran throughout his entire body. His words were offered without **malice** or threat, however, and he continued the thought. "So what do we do? I know, you're tired. Okay, I was once a kid myself. And you need a place to stay. So you're a runaway, Johnny. Okay, great. What does that make me? A fall-guy for teenage **refugees**? No man, I'm just a hard-working guy who doesn't want any more heat than I've already got. Get the message?"

Billy nodded, but his body was once again taking over, his eyes barely able to stay open.

"All right, Johnny, or Joey or whatever your name is. I don't care. I don't want you here tomorrow. Catch my drift? But tonight, you can stay here. I like you. And I don't want to hurt you. And if I knew where you lived, I'd call your folks or your guardian or whoever is responsible for you. You just don't look like a runaway. You don't look that stupid. Suzy does. That's why she was a runaway."

But Billy was already fast asleep and the black man stopped preaching, shaking his head instead. "Sleep well, kid. I really wish I could help you. You're a good-looking boy. Too good to be out here." The door closed, and Billy had the rest of the night to catch up on his sleep and return back home in his dreams.

CHAPTER VII
Final Curtain Call

Sunrise came from the direction of the mountains and produced a greenhouse effect in the glass-windowed room, heating it up at 7:30 a.m. The blazing **radiance** responsible for spectacular and memorable Hawaiian sunsets – but which also made west-facing oceanside rooms a **veritable inferno** in the afternoon – first made clear its **sweltering** presence in the **wee** morning hours to rooms facing east. And for the runaway for whom every precious hour of early-morning sleep was **vital** to better prepare him for the upcoming day of more uncertainty and danger, the **relentless** rays were merciless.

His dreaming was over. The **oppressive** heat was unavoidable and Billy arose from the bed **lethargically** and in a half-**stupor**, drenched in his own perspiration. He looked around instinctively for his clothes, but he wasn't home and he didn't have his school-bag with him in the hotel room.

The television was still on, reminding him of the evening's events, especially the presence of the **imposing** black man. Billy knew he could not stay in the room any longer but felt some relief in at least being allowed the evening to catch up on the rest he well needed.

His immediate need was to use the bathroom, aware that he could also use a shower – or, as was his fortune, a bath. But before all this, he wanted to call Stewart. Maybe his friend hadn't left for school yet.

As he slowly regained a more wakeful consciousness, Billy dialed the number of his most **intimate comrade**. The push-button phone made the dialing too easy – his fingers glided over all the numbers and came up with their own results – and he needed to redial. Finally, after the third time, he completed the number without any errors. The **fatigue** of the previous day continued to **linger**.

"Hello, is Stewart home?...This is, uh, Butch...Yeah, can I please speak with him?...Thank you."

Stewart was still home, and the next few moments would spell out in detail just what impact his disappearance had generated in school.

"Stewart, is that you?" he began after hearing a voice mumble on the other side.

"Billy, where in the heck are you?" Stewart exclaimed, suddenly more alive.

"I'm somewhere in Waikiki. I'm fine, don't worry."

"Worry? Of course I worry. Nobody has seen you in school or anywhere, and you know how rumors go."

"Hello, is Stewart home?"

"What have you heard, Stew?" The excitement of being top-story made Billy feel important, somewhat like a celebrity who had disappeared.

"Nothing, Billy. That's the trouble. I've heard nothing. Nobody's said anything about you. Only rumors. And I haven't heard from your parents or anything. They haven't phoned." There was a momentary silence, then Stewart continued. "Maybe they don't know that you've split, or maybe they've called the cops and nobody knows about it. I really don't know. But really, Snick, why don't you just come on back?"

Billy responded immediately, "No, I wanted to get away and I mean to do it all the way." Then he paused a moment. "Guess what?" he continued in a more lighthearted tone. "I'm staying in a hooker's pad. How about them apples, huh Stew?"

The reaction was not what Billy had expected, however. "Well, Snick, that sounds kinda weird. But I gotta get to school, so I can't talk now. Can you call me after school? I gotta keep in touch with you."

"Sure, Stew, that's why I called," Billy replied seriously. "I'll let you know where I'm at. But I can't give you any phone numbers, 'cause I'm going back out on the road. I'm gonna move on."

"Where?" his friend asked, no longer in the hurry to go to school. "I thought you had a place to stay?"

"Well, it's no good. I didn't come here to get stuck in one place. I want to keep moving."

"Waikiki's such a small place. Where can you go? The cops will spot you in no time."

"Don't worry, Stew. I've kept away for this long, I think I can make it now all the way. Who knows, maybe I'll wind up on the mainland."

The conversation ended abruptly, Stewart's mother yelling at him from the distance. "Sorry, Snick, I gotta go. Call me after school, okay?"

"Sure, Stew."

"Promise?"

"Don't worry about me, Stew. I know what I'm doing."

The final words spoken, Billy hung up the telephone wondering just how much he really knew about what to do next.

The bathroom **beckoned** him and he **executed** his **diurnal hygienic** obligations with **alacrity**. There was even a toothbrush for him, plus a towel and an **array** of soaps, perfumes and body lotions.

Twenty minutes later, Billy was up to his eyes in bubbles. He hadn't taken a bubble-bath since he was in the third grade, and the **sybaritic** experience **engendered** memories **redolent** of the security of his **halcyon** youth, a time when he didn't mind being told what to do and when to do it. "What changed?" he thought to himself. Why was he suddenly **obsessed** with breaking away? If it was just a **whim**, why did it haunt him so much and constantly occupy his thoughts every time his parents would ask him to do something? He had no answers, realizing instead that he was driven to do what he did and was where he really wanted to be. There was no doubt. He wanted to run away, and it was just a matter of time, sooner or later, before he would have done it. Either that or he would have **mutinied** explosively one day and probably have been thrown out, out of the house or out of school. Or even worse, maybe his actions would have led him down the road of **perdition** and eventual **incarceration**.

But fortunately, Billy thought to himself, he had fled to freedom and avoided the **dismal** fate of being forever imprisoned in his parents' **stygian** shelter or worse yet in the **dreaded** State facility. He had never involved himself in drugs, had kept away from the 'bad boys,' and yet he could not **curb** his **quixotic** imagination or disregard all the **piquant scuttlebutt** that **enticed** him and convinced him that the streets offered a more exciting future. He heard it from Butch, from Darren, from a **score** of others who had created such an **alluring** impression of a **vagabond** lifestyle that he could no longer avoid the temptation of experiencing it firsthand. His present **predicament** was therefore unavoidable and the future simply an **inevitable** extension of the unavoidable present. But no matter where the direction led him, Billy felt it would be the best that could happen for him. Even without his clothes and without his friends, the experience was worth every moment. The future looked all the more exciting for Billy as he relaxed in the warm bath and **cogitated** his next moves toward ultimate **deliverance**.

It was 10:30 a.m. when the doorbell rang. Having earlier aired out his clothes, Billy had flopped back on the bed, affording more rest time for himself. He awoke at the bell and **scurried** to **don** his pants and shirt.

"Honey, it's me. Suzy. You can open up the door."

"Coming," he replied, jumping into his clothes. "Just a second, okay?"

"Sure, honey," came the soft answer.

The young lad dashed to the door, then opened it as **nonchalantly** as possible. He didn't want to seem overly anxious, even though he was eager to greet the only person who had really shown genuine **compassion** for him in Waikiki.

"Thanks, Johnny," she added as she entered the room. "Gee, looks like you really had a party here. What'd you do in the bathroom? Put out a fire?"

Billy had neglected to clean up after himself, leaving trails of soapsuds and water streaked about the bathroom, over the mirror and even on the half-open door.

"Sorry, I guess my folks never trained me very well," he justified.

"Honey, that's the biggest understatement I've ever heard. Looks like you've been living with the wolves." But she wasn't angry. The words were issued in a lighthearted tone, an understanding and concerned voice.

"Do I have to leave?" Billy asked directly.

"Why, who ever said that you have to leave? I didn't say that, did I?"

"No, but your boyfriend did."

Suzy was hushed for a brief moment. "Oh, so he did come by? Sorry, but he's really my boss. What did he say to you?"

"Nothing much, except that I've gotta clear out today. But he was cool about it. He's a tough-looking dude."

"He sure is, Johnny, but he's got a heart of gold."

"Yeah, I saw it all over him," Billy added with **jocular** delight, though Suzy apparently didn't **fathom** the **witticism**.

"So where are you going to go, Johnny?" It was obvious that she would not **countermand** her boss, and Billy felt a **twinge** of rejection in the **straightforwardness** of the question.

"Well, I don't know. I was hoping that maybe you..." He paused, staring into her deep brown eyes, trying to **captivate** her with his boyish charm and innocence.

But she didn't fall for the approach. "Johnny, I gotta do what my boss says. I can't help you any more than what I did last night, and I maybe shouldn't have even done that. So maybe you oughta get ready to go."

She then noticed that he had nothing to pack, that he came with only the clothes he was wearing. "Tell you what, Johnny," she said, reaching into her purse, "here's a few twenties. That ought to get you some clothes and some food to last you awhile. And if you run out, just come by and hang outside this place and I'll keep you going, okay? You can always get into the place. Just wait 'til someone goes out or comes in, then you can just wait around outside the room. I'm always going in and out."

"Thanks, ma'm," Billy said with renewed confidence, knowing he had a place to go to if he were in trouble or needed to **replenish** any **depleted** financial reserves.

The door was opened and the traveler walked out slowly, hands in his pockets, into the corridor. He turned to smile at the generous lady, but the door closed almost as soon as he had exited the room. Billy Steele proceeded to the elevator, **contemplating** the afternoon and the rest of his life.

CHAPTER VIII
Back On The Road

The afternoon sun was intense, the cement magnifying its **solar** rays to produce an **intolerable** glare of heat. Billy urgently needed sunglasses but knew he could acquire a pair with minimal effort and no money. He had seen an $80 pair of *Ray-Ban* sunglasses at *Noel's* drug store on the corner, and **absconding** with the **booty** would be easier than tying his shoes. His funds – $120 in twenties – would carry him a long way, especially with his **thriftiness** and ability to survive without needing to spend very much. "The best things in life are free," he advanced, "and *Ray-Bans* are one of the best things in life. Therefore, they should be free." Simple logic, and Billy loved the **rationale**.

The afternoon crowds were **immense**. Tourists had flocked to the island to **revel** and **luxuriate** in the **salubrious** Waikiki sunshine, and with the April season **heralding** the beginning of the long Hawaiian summer the sidewalks and beaches were **rife** with vacationers. This was just the start of the island **migration**, and Billy fit in easily and **inconspicuously** amongst the thousands of men, women and children visitors.

As the make-believe tourist **commenced** his **trek** towards *Noel's*, he experienced an all-too-familiar head-rush feeling that typically began his day, a sensation he thrilled to and **savored**, as though it were that one moment in which the world stopped to afford him an **instantaneous** glimpse into timelessness. It was what he imagined must be **akin** to an **epileptic** seizure, a brilliant split-second of **empyreal effulgence**, of awareness unparalleled. He stopped, looked up at the sunshine and felt the rays **peremptorily** penetrating his nostrils, **suffusing** and **impregnating** his senses with a **potent** surge so **inexorably incapacitating** that he could not think. The pressure built up from within, and he could feel his stomach tightening as his nasal passages prepared for the sudden **jolt**.

To everyone around, it was nothing more than a hearty sneeze, but for Billy it was his welcome to the new day, his 'aloha' for everything that represented the day past and the day yet to come. The event was his reminder that the world was not a repeating record. Every new day, just like every sneeze, was an experience never before imagined, always potentially bigger and better than the one before.

In the course of a few short seconds, Billy had experienced the **cataclysmic** sensation of his whole body reeling to one **momentous** miracle, one **dynamic** and **irrevocable** explosion. Only a sneeze, but for Billy it was a natural 'rush,' a release of inner consciousness that **whetted** his ever-excitable imagination and **induced** it to **conjure** up **innovatively adventuresome machinations**. It was his moment of **rejuvenation**, of rebirth and recognition of his self-identity. Only he could experience the magic, the power of that rush, and as he shook the streets of his soul with the hurricane from within, he **uttered** a soft "Thanks, Lord," **rekindling** the **ritualistic** words he had learned long ago to add after each such **blissful** episode. The **circadian sacrament** had first surfaced when he was eight years old, and though through the years he had **consummated** the event **innumerable** times the ceremony continued to uplift him to a **divinely embryonic equilibrium**, an

equable and undisturbed **placidity** that **emblazoned** his otherwise **plebeian** existence. This time however, the **fleeting** fantasy was rudely interrupted by the **din** of **incessant** chatter and passing cars. Reality had reared its ugly head, and Billy returned to his **mortal** mission; *Noel's* was only two blocks away.

The momentary rush brought new hope to his **quest**, a **revitalized** sense that he was on the right track, that he was 'following his nose.' While everyone else was **shackled** in school, he had broken free. Whatever lay ahead could only be more magnificent than anything that preceded it, guiding him higher, farther beyond what Stewart or Butch or anyone else could ever dream of **realizing**.

The store rapidly appeared, and as he walked in Billy went quickly to work **surveying** the site. The manager was **preoccupied** with a customer, and the sunglasses stood **conspicuously** on the rack adjacent to the counter. It was easy, almost too easy, as though the unguarded merchandise was begging to be taken. Shoplifting had, in fact, become so unchallenging that he had lost the thrill of doing it. When he was in the fifth grade, he **marveled** at the amount of things he could acquire for free, trading them with other friends who'd been successful doing the same thing at other stores. It was like a swap meet, a bargain basement, a garage sale for **barter**. Everything was free, everything was new. But soon the thrill wore off. It became child's play, so easy that it wasn't fun anymore. Friends had said security would eventually tighten up, but it never happened, surely not today at *Noel's*.

Billy was back on the street with his **fancy** new shades, the sun no longer appearing as bright as before. Taking the glasses this time wasn't for **roguish disportment** – it wasn't a kid's game now. For the first time in his life, Billy had stolen something because he actually needed it. The feeling wasn't one of **exhilaration**, merely one of accomplishment. No thrills, just necessity. But with his background experience, the need was easily fulfilled without any bother or worry. Just done, simple as that.

The next problem arose over where he should go. But as Billy **espied** a wet cement slab right next to the bus stop down the street, near *Woolworth*, he realized that a quick decision was not necessary. This was his moment of glory, an opportunity to etch his name and become another of the chosen few to have their identity preserved for the future. In Hollywood, the *Avenue of the Stars* was world-famous, but everywhere there was an *Avenue of the Stars* just waiting to be discovered. And Billy had discovered one right in the heart of Waikiki.

The movie star approached the scene with **tempered insouciance**, sporting his movie-star shades and shaking his hips **à la** *Elvis Presley*. The slab was still wet and nobody was interested in walking near the **cordoned** off section of the sidewalk. Billy was alone and free to begin his masterpiece. "Take it easy...Billy da cruise..." he traced with two fingers. He then drew with **celerity** a picture of a wave breaking perfectly, symbolizing the ideal lifestyle of the 'cruiser beachboy': riding the perfect waves in Hawaii.

Billy was back on the street...

The wave was the symbol of independence, reflecting a lifestyle in which rules did not apply. The day was for surfing, the night for thinking about the surf, and the next morning for going back out into the surf. Nothing more. Nothing else was necessary. No hassles, no money-problems, only surf and cruise. It was what every eighth-grader wanted, and he found himself chosen to be the spokesman on this hot, summery Hawaiian Friday, the day before his friends would go to the beaches and look for the perfect waves. Maybe they'd see his artwork and know that Billy had indeed found what he was looking for.

Waikiki was fast becoming a **burgeoning** paradise for the young pioneer. The engraving **infused** his **indefatigable** imagination with yet more energy, more power and more hope. Whatever he was to do, it would be perfect. The wave was his symbol, and he had discovered it and preserved it today. There was a definite purpose for this to have happened.

"Okay you, off that," came a **bellowing** voice from above. Billy stared up at two people he needed to fear the most. A police car had pulled up next to him, its blue lights flashing. "Come over here," the policeman in the passenger seat called roughly.

Billy **heeded** the call. He could never run from two policemen in Waikiki, not in the middle of the day. "Yes, sir?" was all he could produce.

"Drawing graffiti in the cement, huh? Where do you live?" The policeman took out his paper and pencil.

"Oh, I'm here on vacation. I live in the high-rise with my mother. I don't know the name, but it's room 1426." The words flowed so smoothly and convincingly that the officer offered no challenge to what Billy had said.

"Okay, but get back to where you belong. Your mom would get pretty mad at you, probably beat you up, if we were to tell her what you just did."

"No she wouldn't," Billy **interjected emphatically**, defending Suzy, "She's a nice person and I don't think she'd ever hit me."

The officer was visibly moved by the reply. "Sorry, kid. I've got a mom myself. Just stay out of trouble, that's all." He then paused briefly, eyeing Billy with admiration. "You're a nice kid. Hardly nobody says that about their mom anymore. You're a lucky kid, and your mom's a lucky mom." He then added in a playful tone, "Now beat it before I begin to treat you like my own kid." He drew out a dollar and reached it over to Billy. "Here, take it and get yourself an ice-cream cone. Then you can keep out of trouble for a while, okay?"

"Gee thanks, sir," Billy replied somewhat confused. He had made friends with the least likely of people, **consorting** with a prostitute and now a policeman. Nothing seemed to make sense, so Billy just nodded and walked away, trying to figure out where the nearest ice-cream store was so he could

This was his moment of glory...

47

satisfy the man's request and escape from the near-disaster.

The police car proceeded onwards along the strip, both policemen waving politely while driving by. As they passed out of sight, Billy regained his **bearing** and, slipping the dollar into his pocket with the rest of the money, looked toward his next destination. It was Friday, it was afternoon. There was only one place he could think of at this **opportune** moment. He headed for the *Waikiki Video Factory*.

CHAPTER IX
Unpleasant Reunion

The glitter of the machines never changed. They always **fluoresced** in a **fey** light, producing a hypnotic effect which made a person forget about his troubles, about the world outside, about time itself. *Dragon's Lair*, *The Mighty Hulk*, *Galaxians*, *Moon Cresta*, *The Force*, they all were little worlds into which a person could escape. One instantly became a warrior, or a boxer, or *Sylvester Stallone* or whoever one wanted to be. The *Video Factory* was a fairy-tale land for those who sought the **solace** of their own *Xanadu*. For Billy, it was the perfect **apotheosis** of **asylums**, the perfect escape from the hustle and bustle of the streets outside.

As long as he had quarters to play the machines, he was welcome in the *Video Factory*; and with the **cache** he had in his pocket he knew he could long remain **immersed** in these foreign fantasy lands if only he could continue to **elude** the police. But fortunately for him, they seldom entered video establishments except after the 10:00 p.m. **curfew**, when they were responsible for clearing the streets of all minors under the age of fifteen. Were he in a **suburb** of Honolulu, the police would check to see that no **truants** were **frequenting** the site, but here in Waikiki – where tourists, young and old, **predominated** the scene – they would have a difficult time **distinguishing** between **truant** teens and those on vacation. And with the tourist-dollar such an **integral** part of Hawaii's economy, the police were quick to remind themselves that their job was not to **antagonize** anyone while in pursuit of **derelict** schoolkids. It was therefore best for them to just avoid arousing any such **indignation**, and thus one would rarely see a policeman enter the premises during the day.

Billy had the rest of the afternoon to 'space out,' and he found himself **engrossed** for an hour in one of his favorite games, *Mappy*, when he felt a tapping on his shoulder. He shrugged off the touch, but when it persisted he responded. "Yeah, just a second. Wait 'til I finish this one screen."

But the tapping **recurred**, this time with more emphasis. Billy turned around, **fearful** that it might be a policeman. Then his game would surely be over. But it wasn't a cop. It was worse. It was Sam Herman.

"Well, well, well, so you decided to stop your game. Gee, that's nice." The tone was far from friendly underneath the polite **veneer**. "I thought I might find you here one day, sonny boy. And from what I hear, you haven't been around, have you? Kind of like you just disappeared?"

Billy stared up at the **hulking** six-foot **Herculean titan** who towered above him as he sat, soda in hand, in the video chair. Herman was the 'bruiser,' the eleventh-grader whose favorite pastime was breaking things. Sometimes chairs, sometimes windows, sometimes bones. Whether he was on the football field or in class, he was always a potential threat. Just shaking hands with him could become a regrettable experience. But at this moment Sam was not in the mood for friendly handshakes. His closed fist smacking decisively against his right hand made clear his intentions. Billy was faced with his least favorite form of communication. And he knew he would not emerge the **victor**. No words could prevent the showdown, and the comparatively slim blond boy regretted

It was Sam Herman.

all the words of **provocation** he had thrust out against Sam Herman in the past. Herman was now there to collect for all that was said. He was *Shylock*, and Billy represented the pound of flesh about to be taken as **recompense**.

"Can we talk about it, Sam?" Billy **beseeched**.

"Sure. Why don't we go outside behind the building, and then you can tell me that you're sorry. That sounds fair."

But Billy knew these words were a mere **façade** for what Sam Herman really had in mind. Herman's fist continued its **melodic** thumping, the sound echoing and increasing in volume. Billy's eyes were glued to the fist hitting the hand.

"Face it, punk," he continued, "you're stuck this time. Take it and it won't hurt so much." And with those final words he raised Billy up, grabbing his shoulder with one hand. The eighth grader was off the chair and on his feet, no resistance able to stop the force of the 'bruiser.'

Billy **contemplated** his options. He could yell, but that would attract attention, possibly the police, and probably only make his future with Sam even more **precarious**. Or he could try to run. But Sam now had his arm well **secured**. The only option remaining would be to try to talk his way out of it, seizing any opportunity to flee once he was led outside the building. Amid the crowds of Waikiki, he could easily get away without creating much **ado**. Sam would be faced with no alternative but to seek him another day, in another place. The police would not be involved, and thus his **imbroglio** with Sam would not be **exacerbated** through a show of desperate **histrionics**. Billy would get away, sweet and simple. The **pernicious predator** might **stalk** him another day, but for now he would be free and more **vigilant** to **avert** any such future **encounters**.

"Okay, Sam, I'll go. But can we talk about it first?"

Sam continued his **superficial** dialogue. "Sure, punk, you talk and I'll listen. And then you can listen to me, okay?"

"Yeah, sure Sam." Billy felt somewhat relieved. Perhaps Sam seriously wanted to discuss it with him; however, this was a gamble Billy did not plan to take. Instead, he had but one course of action in mind: once free, his feet would do the talking, one long run-on sentence out to the sidewalk and to freedom.

The two walked slowly out the front door, Herman's hand firmly gripping Billy's left arm near the shoulder. As they approached the sidewalk, Herman suddenly pulled the youngster back towards the stairwell that lay adjacent to the video parlor. Before Billy knew what had happened, he was inside the stairwell, the door closing behind him. He had nowhere to run. Sam Herman **glowered** at him as he twisted the boy's arm and forced him to the ground.

"Now we can talk," the **redoubtable antagonist** began. "We got a lot to talk about, don't we, Spit. So talk."

Billy just stared up defenselessly, helplessly waiting for Sam to do something, whether to inflict some bone-crushing blow or just continue to **wrench** his arm until it would fall off. "I'm sorry, Sam," he **whimpered**, hoping that the apology would **propitiate** the **behemoth** and **defuse** the **grave** situation. But such kid-games were for playing at home, under the bed-covers, where dreams and fantasies were at one's **disposal**. Here in the streets, in the middle of nowhere, dreams were inappropriate and hope was **ineffectual**. This was no time to pretend.

Seconds turned to minutes, Sam stalling for some reason; he just stood there, looking down at Billy as though ready to kick him at any moment but **stifling** the urge. Then suddenly the stairwell door opened and four other **burly** teenagers quickly entered. Billy didn't recognize them in their cutoff shirts and Bermuda shorts, but he **surmised** that they were fellow football players, friends of the 'bruiser.'

"So that's the twerp?" one of the pack said. He had a sly, **sinister** look, as though about to enjoy a hearty dinner, with Billy as the main course.

"Did he really run away?" another of the pack asked. "Well, I think we can make it really look that way, huh Sam?"

"Just shut up and get the stuff," the hostile hostage-taker replied **brusquely**. One of the pack reached into a duffel bag and pulled out what appeared to be a **syringe** of some sort.

Sam addressed his next words to Billy. "You think everyone's watching you, huh? You think just because you got a stupid smile, you can turn the world around and make everyone like you. Well, that ain't the way it is, Spit. And for every injury that put me closer to the needle, it's been **puny** punks like you who try to trash me that really get on my nerves. I've wasted myself for Palmview. I've had enough bones broke to say that I've almost died for my school. And it's scum like you who make the school look cheap, make me look cheap. But I don't take that crap from no one. You want to know how I feel? Do you, huh Spit?"

Sam **glared** down at Billy, Snick looking up **fearfully** and in deadly silence. Sam was determined to say what he wanted, and no response was needed or requested.

"Jake, give me that needle," Herman commanded one of the boys. Once received, he pointed it at Billy. "This stuff, my friend, is what I'm hooked on. It's heavy stuff and I've got to take it for the pain. But you, little **scrawny** twerp, you're gonna take it 'cause it's here and you're here. And when we're done with you, you'll be a true junkie. And then it'll be my turn to laugh when I see you around. Hope you like it." And with that, Sam drew the **syringe** closer towards Billy, whose artificial struggling served little purpose.

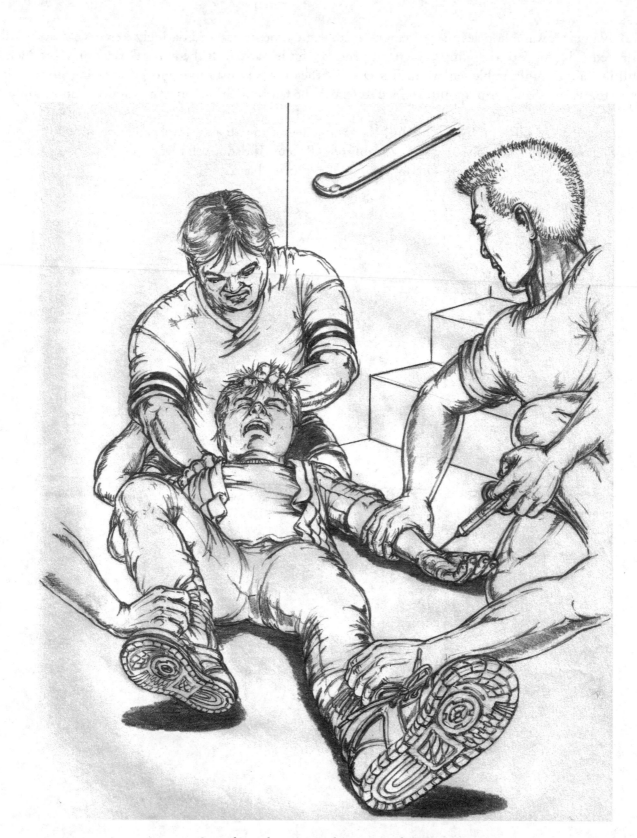

Sam drew the syringe closer towards Billy...

53

Billy knew it was a hopeless situation, but at the same time he **yearned** daringly to see what the needle contained. He stopped struggling as he felt it penetrate his left arm near the wrist, the chemical producing a burning, almost unbearable sensation. The effect of the drug was **instantaneous**. Everything around him started to **gyrate**. Sam's grip on him seemed to relax as he felt himself floating on a cloud of uncertainty.

The feeling was unclear. It wasn't a thrill, it wasn't a depression. It was simply an **enervating** numbness. He felt relaxed, totally at peace, in a state of **sublime solitude**. The stairwell turned a bright shade of white, then orange, and finally it began to disappear. Then all turned black.

CHAPTER X
The Dawn

When Billy opened his eyes, he found himself looking up into the sky, his head pounding and his stomach sore. He wasn't in the stairwell anymore but instead on a rooftop of a Waikiki high-rise, thirty stories above the **clamor** and commotion of the tourist traffic. In a semi-panic, the first thing he thought to remember was his name. Billy Steele. A sigh of relief came over him as he confirmed to himself that he was still in control of his senses. His clothes were all still **intact**, but his stomach was sore, his ribs hurt, and his entire lower body was **racked** with pain. **Assessing** his physical and mental state, Billy reflected upon what might have happened to him, considering any number of possible **scenarios**. **Excruciating** though the pain was, it was **tempered** somewhat by the **sedating** effect of the drug which still **permeated** his body and swelled within his head.

In his half-conscious state, Billy sensed an immediate need to climb down the stairs rather than risk falling off the building. He stumbled towards the stairwell, tripped and landed flat on his stomach atop the gravel floor of the roof, exhausted and too tired to move. He lay there motionless as sleep once more overcame him, offering a temporary **respite** from the **acute** discomfort. The teenager lifted his head one last time in **vain**, then collapsed into uncontested **oblivion**.

After an eternity of sleep, Billy once again opened his eyes. It was morning, and the air was cold and damp. He **essayed** standing up but in his dizzy and **debilitated** state **balked** at the **arduous endeavor**. Instead, he raised his head weakly and grasped for a railing, but his hands felt nothing and his face fell helplessly back upon the ground.

"Long night, eh?" a soft female voice called to him from nearby.

Billy tried to turn to see who the person was, but he couldn't move. The voice sounded sweet and youthful, but what he needed now was more than a young girlfriend. He needed some warm food and a **sobering** hot bath.

"I feel awful," he finally replied. "I think I'm sick, I think I'm stoned, and I don't know what I'm doing here."

"Right, friend. Just like me." The person then approached Billy and turned him over, staring into his deep blue eyes. "You're a pretty boy, you know that. I like your eyes. Except that they look kinda weird. Whatcha been taking?"

Billy stared up blankly. "I don't know. Some guys gave it to me."

"Well, it looks pretty strong, the way it hit you. But don't worry, I'll get you to my pad and you can sleep it off there."

"No, that's okay," he replied quickly. "Just leave me alone. I don't want to move right now.

Please leave me alone."

"You want me to get you out of here or not?" The girl was **steadfast** and insistent.

Billy focused his eyes upon her, though unable to see her clearly. He realized that she represented the only help he'd be receiving and knew better than to further decline her **timely** and **providential** assistance. "Okay, but I don't know if I can stand up."

"Don't worry, friend. I'll be back with my...brother. We'll get you out of here."

Billy watched wearily as the young woman headed for the stairs, his mind still **stupefied** and his body equally **enfeebled** by the drug's **hallucinogenic potency**. Within seconds, he found himself fading off into unconsciousness for what seemed a second eternity.

When he awoke, he was no longer on the top of the building; he was now on a bed in a small room. With his head propped up against a pillow, Billy could easily survey the new scenery. The **lone** window reflected a dark shade, indicating twilight beyond. There were no lights in the room, and the **drabness** of the off-white walls, combined with the cloak of **impending** darkness from outside, cast upon the room a **sallow, lugubrious pall**. In the far corner he **espied** a **solitary** and almost **adventitiously** appearing coffee table which served no purpose. It merely occupied space, filling a tiny portion of a greater **void** which the whole room seemed to **metaphorically embody**.

As the young stranger pursued his inspection of the property, he could feel his head **undulating** as though he had just come off a roller coaster ride. The **gyrations** came with such **ferocity** that he soon lay back, **resigning** himself to **quell** his curiosity rather than risk becoming **nauseous** from the overpowering **vertigo**.

As he rested, Billy **pondered** his present **disposition** and **cogitated** upon his future direction. He had sought unrestricted freedom of movement, but **ironically** he could now barely move his head. He was in an **immobile stupor**, though his mind was conscious and his thoughts somewhat clear. The sensation was comparable to the helplessness of a person on life-support, able mentally to comprehend but unable physically to respond. The disabling numbness sent a shudder of panic throughout his body. But it didn't help. He still couldn't move. The **apoplectic vulnerability** left him like a baby in the midst of wolves, and he knew it. He had been **subjugated** by a force he knew nothing about, and the next **telling** developments would not be of his own **volition**. He awaited the arrival of his visitors, anticipating **adversaries** but silently praying for some **benign patrons**.

Several minutes passed, then Billy heard the door creak open. As he very slowly opened his eyes and gazed upward, he recognized the face as that of the gracious **benefactor** who had given **succor** to him in his most critical time of need, and as she **peered** intensely into his cloudy blue eyes his inability to react made him once again feel helpless and dependent.

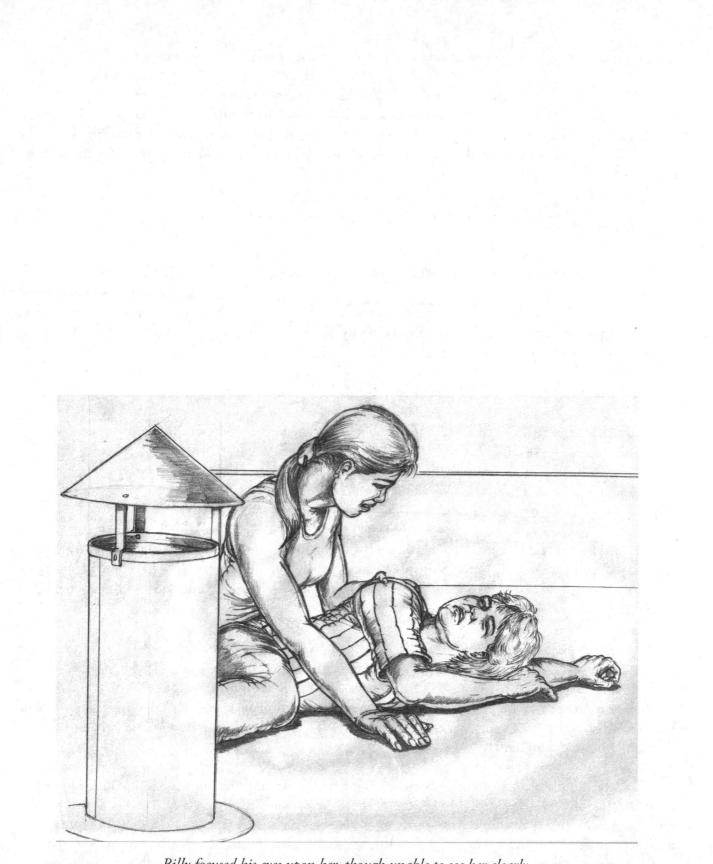

Billy focused his eyes upon her, though unable to see her clearly.

"Are you okay, Billy?" the young lady asked in a **compassionately** concerned voice.

"I...I think so," he replied uncertainly. She had apparently **ascertained** his name through their conversation, but the familiarity did not help to **ameliorate** the **unrelenting reverberations** which sought to drive him to madness. With each word he spoke, the hammering became more **excruciating**, so for the sake of his own sanity he avoided further **discourse**, closing his eyes instead and praying for the **serenity** of sleep.

"My name is Sandy," the **benevolent** stranger resumed. "I've got my brother here. He's Tom. Can you hear me, Billy?"

Billy replied with urgent **brevity**. "Yeah. What's happening to me?"

"You've had an overdose, Billy," came a low voice beside Sandy. "I think my sister got to you just in time. I'm brewing some coffee, and when you can raise your head, try to drink as much as you can. I don't know what you took, but you didn't take it well."

"Can you hear us, Billy?" Sandy asked once again.

"Yeah, I hear you. I'm listening." Billy wanted to hear more, more about his hosts, more about his overdose, more about his future. He was all ears.

"Tom and I want to help you. We've been in Hawaii for a while and we've seen what's happening to young kids like you. We want to help you. Do you understand that?"

Her social **solicitude** seemed oddly **anachronistic**, as though she were an anti-war leftover from some television documentary of the '60s. She was obviously not as young as she first looked, nor as young as she sounded. Her words **bespoke** a wisdom earned with age, and her brother continued on the same train of thought.

"There's a lot you can do for us. There's a lot we can do for you. But first of all, try to get better. I'll get you the coffee and then you can try to get your head cleared up. Okay?"

Billy tried to nod, but the violent **vortex** of his mental **maelstrom** once again forced him into **submission**. Perceiving the critical nature of the **convulsive malady**, Tom exited immediately for the kitchen to retrieve the freshly-brewed **stimulant**.

The **odoriferous** aroma of coffee beans brought back morning memories of Billy's mom preparing breakfast for him and his dad. Billy would arrive first, casually feasting on *Frosted Flakes*, his dad arriving five minutes later in a rush and with little time to eat. Rather than a morning family get-together, however, it more closely resembled a race to the finish line. His dad would spend a few seconds chopping the top off his soft-boiled egg and putting the grape jelly on his two slices of toast, and then he would stuff it down his gullet, drowning the food with the coffee. All his

"My name is Sandy. I've got my brother here. He's Tom."

59

mother's **conscientious** and **meticulous culinary** preparations went for **naught**, his father **voraciously** consuming the **viands** as thoughtlessly as though **quaffing** a pitcher of beer. Breakfast was always played out in this **chaotic melodrama**, a senseless **scenario** in which nothing **constructive** was communicated to **commemorate** the **communion** or **relish** the **regalement** of a **recherché repast** shared socializing spiritedly with one's spouse and **progeny**.

As Billy **ruminated** the **rueful** daily **disaffection**, Tom brought in the **aromatically** arousing and **potent** potion, and the youngster awakened to its arrival. Sandy **gingerly** moved the cup to the lad's mouth and let him sip it slowly and carefully. The coffee tasted good. It was only the third time he had ever tasted coffee, the first time that the taste was satisfying. If only his father could have enjoyed it half as much, Billy might never have left home.

"How are you feeling now?" Sandy asked as she noticed the color returning to the young boy's face. "You're looking better."

She was right. The pounding was slowly **dissipating** and he could now move his head without the **incapacitating** attending dizziness.

"You finish the cup, then get some rest," Tom continued. "We'll talk some more in the morning."

Billy opened his eyes, staring confusedly at the two **divine** liberators. "Thanks for helping me."

"Don't mention it," Tom replied. "You'll be helping us soon enough."

Billy tried to evaluate the words he heard but found himself overcome by a much-needed **repose**. The future would have to wait until tomorrow.

CHAPTER XI
The Dream

The sounds of mynahs chirping in the morning grass awakened the voyager from a land of dreams. For the first time in months, Billy had dreamed of his distant island, a dream which **recurred** frequently and produced for him the most **desolately serene** of moments. The island was small and deserted, and the only sounds that interrupted his **pensive** thoughts were the **plaintive** call of sea gulls and the splashing of waves against the sandy shore. He was alone and undisturbed, lying on a tiny beach fronting three-foot waves which crashed rhythmically, in perfect **cadence**.

The sun shone brightly and warmly down upon him, and as he faced the **azure** skies he could feel the tingle of the rays **caress** his chest, awakening in him a feeling too secret to share with others. He was in his own world, free from others' evaluation, others' ridicule. It was his dream, his island, his world. No one else was there, no one else was allowed there. Not his parents, not even his friends. Maybe Stewart, though he never appeared in the dream. Billy was at one with nature, alone to open his imagination to all the visions that lay above, before, and all around him. He lay in peace upon the tiny island with its **pristine** yellow-sand beach and its sloping hill **lush** with **verdant** shrubbery. It was his island, meant only for him, **vast** enough to require several minutes to **traverse** yet small enough to view in its entirety from atop the twenty-five-foot hilltop. A small island, but an entire world, and he was in control. All that existed was for him. The **solitude**, the **placidity**, the freedom all **infused** in him a sense of pride and fulfillment that fame and fortune could never **rival**. It was only a dream, but its image was more real than any video parlor game. He was not a participant in his dreams; he was the overseer. He had purpose, a reason to be there. He was the guardian, the **curator** of the island, and nature was his **beacon**. It all seemed so real and spiritually meaningful that he would often try to **retain** the mental image even in his wakeful hours.

The welcome vision had been absent for months, the magic of the dreamlike **bliss** fading with each passing day. But now it had returned, and Billy awoke with a smile and a prayer of thanks to the **supernal** powers that had afforded him this **visitation** to a better world.

"How are you feeling, Billy?" Sandy asked in a **cordial** manner as she walked through the open door, carrying a tray of food. "You were zonked out last night, but I can see you've made a really impressive recovery."

"Thanks..." Billy answered, still not remembering the lady's name. "By the way, how did I get into these clothes?" He could feel that he was wearing pajamas, though he hadn't looked under the sheets to confirm how they looked. "And this sweatshirt, it's really nice."

"Thanks, Billy. That's one of Tom's, so it's probably too big for you. But then again, it all shrinks when you've washed it enough times, so I guess it probably doesn't fit either of you very well."

Billy lifted the sheets, **peering** at his blue *Bermudas*, not exactly what he had expected to see.

"Gee, these are really cool. I thought they were pajamas. You really know how to make a guy dress in style." He suddenly felt a **twinge** of embarrassment and blushed, realizing that he hadn't **donned** the clothes himself. Sandy sensed his **discomposure**.

"Oh don't worry, Billy. You were so out of it that I just helped get you **spruced** up and washed up a bit. But I'll tell you," she added quietly, "you're cute under those clothes."

Billy flashed back to his dream. Somewhere in the midst of it, sometime when he was feeling his supreme happiest, this gentle, **compassionate** person was probably at that very moment undressing him. It had to be so. The dream simply didn't reappear by coincidence. He felt a bit ashamed and yet a bit **invigorated**, all at the same time. It was indeed a fantasy, a real and **vivid** one, one he desperately **longed** to return to again.

"Thanks, ma'm, for helping me," Billy added **coyly**.

"The name's 'Sandy', okay?"

"Thanks, Sandy," he repeated politely. Billy had at last been able to **utter** her name, the name of a woman he had no intention of ever forgetting, for no other person had ever gotten so physically close to him before. He **disdained** physical contact, except if it were **incidental** such as on a football field or in wrestling. His personal space was **inviolate**, and he **spurned** all advances that **encroached** upon this **hallowed** and **sacrosanct domain**. But Sandy had indeed trespassed, and yet he admitted her without **reserve**. He was unconscious then, but now he was awake and **harbored** no **ill will** toward her for what she had done for him. She had helped him when he was unable to **fend** for himself, and in this golden moment of need he had found a friend who gave without taking, who offered herself without demanding something in return. In the course of a dream, Sandy had become his most **intimate** acquaintance.

"Here's something to eat, Billy. I'll have your clothes washed and dry for you soon, so just relax and get your energy back. The bathroom's out the hall and to the right. Also, there's a shower if you like." She paused for a moment to allow Billy time to **digest** the information. "You can call this your new home if you want to. I know Tom's happy you came here. In fact, there's so much we can talk about. Like what happened to you and all that."

Billy nodded his head confusedly while Sandy spoke. She then reached the tray down to Billy and kissed him tenderly on his forehead, just below his wavy blond hair. The kiss burned itself into him, warming his inside as the coffee had done the evening before. So much was happening so fast. The dream, his new clothes, his new home, a kiss. He tried to speak, but his words froze. Sandy placed two fingers upon his lips and whispered "Don't speak, Billy. Just believe." And then the **seraphic** inspiration withdrew softly and left Billy alone to feast upon a **cornucopia** of **comestibles**: bacon and eggs, orange juice and an English muffin **adorned** with apricot preserves. For the young man, it was an **ambrosial** delight fit for a king.

The mynahs chirped as they **foraged** for food, but Billy was no longer out in the wild seeking **sustenance**. He had found his new home. He no longer needed to depend on strangers for security. "Keep yelling, birds," he called out, "and maybe I'll throw you some bread when I'm done."

The **rhapsodic reverie** of his exclusive island paradise resurfaced as he **ruminated** on his enviable fortune. He had at long last found his *Shangri-la*, and its sea gulls were now mynah birds. He had **realized** his goal of **attaining** personal freedom and was in control of his own **destiny**. But for now, the future didn't matter. He was **immersed** in his own **nirvana** and **opted** instead to **revel** in this moment of dream-come-true **splendor**.

The hearty meal was **savory** and **palatable**, but rather than follow it up with a **brisk** shower to **sober** up and return to the material world, Billy elected to go back to sleep, to **perchance** return to his island and hope that Sandy would be there to join him. He placed the tray with the empty plates and glass atop a small **nondescript** bedside table that lay **inconspicuously** within reach, then snuggled under the covers and awaited the calm surrender of sleep to transport him back to his private world, a world now made for two.

CHAPTER XII
A New Team

In the couple of days that followed, Billy gained a fuller understanding of and appreciation for Sandy and Tom, their activities with the underground and their **aversion** for many of the ideals that democracy had come to represent.

"Sure, Billy," Tom said during dinner one evening, "you can do anything you want in today's society. You can smoke yourself to death, you can get beaten up on any street you like, and you can get drugged anytime you like. If that's what 'freedom' is, I don't like it and I don't need it. It's part of the **capitalistic** plot. You think you're living in heaven but really you're just being milked dry by taxes so the rich can **gorge** themselves. No, it's not what you were told it was, Billy. It's a **deceptive illusion**. It's an excuse to keep you from finding out who really runs the ship. I mean, it's *Watergate* every day of the year. Somebody on top is always taking advantage of people on the bottom. And Billy, that's you and that's me. We're the victims. But we haven't been defeated. That's why Sandy and I are here. That's why you're here."

Tom loved to **pontificate** over social misfortunes, **inveighing** against a political system whose **rapacious lust** for power **fostered** the **venal corruption** and **abridgment** of **dissenting** opinions. Billy **earnestly assayed** the validity of Tom's **vociferous vituperations** against democracy, yet couldn't relate with the **exasperation** of living in a free land. Had Tom ever been to a communist country? Billy **queried** quietly. The issue was nevertheless **moot** to Billy, who was instead grateful to Tom for offering him shelter, food and companionship. The least he could do in return was hear his host out and **indulge** his **unorthodox** political **ideology**, **tenets** which seemed to come straight out of '60s rock songs he had heard so many times on the radio. The ideas were like playbacks of old *Peter, Paul & Mary* songs or something that the *Rolling Stones* might have echoed early in their career. But such **antiquated** and **dogmatic declamatory doctrine** simply wasn't **apropos** in an age of computers and video games, Billy **contended** in silence, a new age in which people eagerly **embraced** the opportunities of the future, not **obsessed** upon the **iniquities** of the past.

Billy merely **brooked** Tom's **digressive diatribes** with **feigned** interest, and Tom accepted the listening ear of his young **proselyte** with a **sententious smugness**. Sandy, meanwhile, was always **diligently** occupied with cleaning dishes or preparing meals – avoiding Tom's long-winded and **diffuse recitations** – then slipping away for a couple of hours at a time in the evening as if entertaining a secret **rendezvous** or perhaps delivering top-secret information to an **insurgent** group **engaged** in **espionage**.

Her whereabouts became known to Billy on the third evening, while he was resting comfortably, watching TV and chewing on a *Butterfinger*.

"Well, Tom," she exclaimed, **bounding** through the door **gleefully**, "this time we got the big one." She was all smiles, slapping her hands against her knees as if doing the *Charleston* in **mock** fashion, acting like a schoolgirl. Billy turned from the couch he was sitting on and grinned playfully. "Gee, you can share it with me. I won't tell anyone."

Sandy then hopped over to Billy and sat atop his lap. "My dear, sweet boy, if you weren't so cute, I think I'd kiss you."

"What's stopping you?" Billy dared.

And with that invitation, Sandy placed her lips squarely upon Billy's and planted a kiss so powerful that she practically sucked all the air out of his lungs.

Billy fell back against the cushion, both amazed and shocked by the intensity of her affection. He had kissed a few girls in his young life, but no girl had ever **initiated** contact with him and surely no one had ever before left him so **utterly dumbfounded** and **nonplussed** by aggressively **bestowing** such a **torridly passionate token** of **esteem**. His stomach began to growl and his body began to twitch as though a **tempest** was slowly brewing from within, seeking an outlet to escape. He had felt this way before, but never to this extent. His blue eyes closed softly as he sought to **suppress** the feeling of young passion. If this was love, he was still too young to respond to it. Instead, he elected to try to let it pass without **stoking** the flame further. He surely wouldn't dare Sandy to try that again. Not unless Tom wasn't around.

"So you got the big message out, huh Twinkle?" Tom asked, disregarding the silent spectacle.

"Yeah, Monk, sure did. The biggest wall you've ever seen. Flat out across the whole thing. As big as an elephant."

By now, Billy's curiosity was beside himself. He had to find out what had produced such **rapture** for his **fair damsel**.

"What did you do, Twinkle?" he asked shyly.

"Don't call me 'Twinkle,' not unless you got a nickname that I can call you, sweetie," Sandy replied in a **sportive** manner.

"Call me 'Snicker.' That's my nickname...Twinkle."

Sandy burst out with laughter. "'Snicker,' I love that name. You're like candy, sweet and full of nuts." She and Tom **snickered** at Sandy's description, but Billy wasn't **impressed**. No one had ever made fun of his nickname, and he felt uncomfortable that Tom was laughing along with Sandy, at him.

"Oh, don't worry, Snicker," Sandy added, detecting Billy's irritation. "What I mean is, you're just perfect. And that name fits you, too. I don't know how I ever managed to find you, but I guess it was just kismet.

Sandy hopped over to Billy and sat atop his lap.

Billy was satisfied with Sandy's attempted apology. She had a way of stroking his **ego** and making him feel so special that **assuaged** any **residual indignation**. Billy could **foster** no **resentment** against a girl as honest and down-to-earth as she was. Instead, he pursued the matter of her **felicity**.

"What did you do? Rob a bank?"

"Oh, my dear silly young man, that would be **capitalistic**, and that's the root of all evil. No, I did more. I painted our slogan right across the back of the *Hotel Waikiki*. The perfect place to express our feelings."

"You mean 'graffiti'!" Billy cried. "I thought that's just for kids."

"'Kids?'" Sandy asked, **astounded**. "You think it's a kid's game? My oh my, where have you been all your life? Haven't you ever looked closely at what it all says? Most of it is art, a **clarion** call to arms against the **capitalistic propaganda** that floods people's minds. It's 'Truth,' not what you read in **sordidly sensationalistic** newspapers and see in **saccharine** news stories **extenuating** government **malfeasance**. It's the only place you can really see what the people think!" The **loquacious** lass had flown off on a **tangent**, just as Tom did so often, but her **exuberance** was contagiously **captivating** and Billy perked up to hear more of her **riveting exploits**.

"It's in three colors, and it says 'No Business Today, As Usual.' It's the ultimate truth about **capitalism**. I'll bring you over to see it, Billy. And you too, Tom."

Tom nodded in approval, but Billy just stared at Sandy somewhat in disbelief. "Is she for real?" he thought to himself. Or was this just an adult gag to make him start laughing. No sooner did the second thought pass through his mind than he realized Sandy and Tom were serious. The sign-drawing had **vivified** their personalities and was indeed the highlight of the day for both of them. And yet, what value did it serve? What satisfaction could they possibly gain from what Sandy had done? Billy **mulled over** a **multitude** of possible answers to his **sundry** questions, but one question remained unasked, one which aroused his curiosity, one which he felt **compelled** to finally ask. Somewhat out of envy for what **exultation** and **bliss** they had created for themselves, he finally proposed the **crowning** question. "Can I join you?" Billy bit his upper lip, dying for a positive response.

"We thought you'd never ask," Tom replied, smiling. The two adults nodded approvingly at one another, and Billy knew he had been accepted as a member of their family.

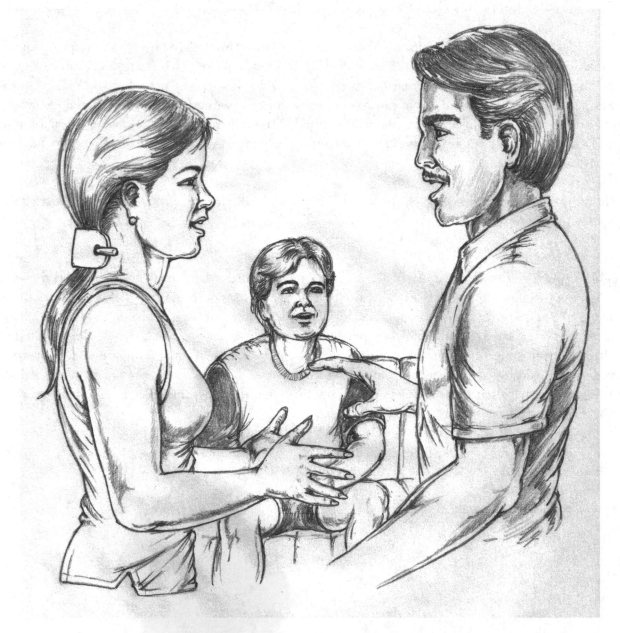

"Can I join you?"

CHAPTER XIII
New Perspectives

The next few days became an educational experience for Billy, as though he were back in school but taking courses he had never heard of before. Instead of History, he studied American **Corruption**; in place of Art, there was Creative-Expression Writing. Sandy and Tom familiarized him with their past, their involvement with **anti-apartheid** protests, anti-nuclear marches, anti-*Reagan* rallies, anti-everything events. The two seemed to **thrive** on anything opposed to the **Establishment**, and the urge to be different rang in harmony with Billy's sentiments. He had always wanted to break away and had now discovered a group that shared the same beliefs. They were more grown-up in their methods of expressing themselves, but the restlessness and discontent with the **status quo transformed** the two adults into kids, much like Billy himself.

The **motley** trio became **compatriots** in a war against **mediocrity**, **rekindling** the spirit of the hippy movement of the sixties and the social **unrest prevalent** during the *Viet Nam* era. Tom recalled stories of their activities as far back as the mid-sixties, Billy discovering that these two were long-time **veterans** of their trade. In their **comradeship** Billy found himself as a young warrior, a **tyro** in a new field of **endeavor**, pursuing the ambitious goal of expressing himself to the world, on behalf of the family. Their purposeful mission fascinated him, and he **revered** his two **mentors** from whom he would learn the art of illustrative **iconoclastic insurrection**. In return, he was treated as royalty, **epitomizing** the **seditiously subversive** poster-child for a new generation. He was their **protégé**, and in **solidarity** the trio **collaborated** to make a deep impression upon Waikiki. Freedom would again **prevail**.

Billy's confinement in the house was far from boring. Along with food and shelter, he was entertained with television, conversation and numerous books and magazines which contained chapters and articles relating to their movement, which they **aptly** called *The Eve of Destruction*. Their **quasi-mantra ode** was Barry McGuire's **cautionary** ballad from the early years of *Viet Nam*, a song whose **profound invocation** for social and moral reevaluation seemed as **relevant** as the day it was first penned. Billy was more amazed, day by day, by how much the two eras had in common. The hippy protest movement had indeed never died; it simply lay **dormantly** awaiting the world's **retrogression** to the same **precarious plight** it was in thirty years earlier. Tom and Sandy were a living **testament** to the **indomitable** individual spirit, and Billy envied their ability to stay young-at-heart and still have a dream, a purpose in life, amid all the **chaos** around them.

While Tom and Sandy were shopping one afternoon, Billy thought of relating his latest **aspirations** by calling Stewart. He had learned so much so quickly and had become so consumed in his new **apprenticeship** that he had not thought about contacting his old friends or even worrying about his parents. But after all that he had learned, with all he had yet to accomplish, he now hungered to share the news with someone.

The young warrior picked up the receiver, wondering what he would say. What would Stewart have to say to him? His high **anxiety** was quickly **allayed**, however, when he realized he had nothing to be worried about, nothing to fear from the world he'd left behind. He had survived the daring escape and was now safe from the dangers that most runaways face daily. And he didn't need to escape anymore, for he had found **deliverance** living in the safety and shelter of **allies**. Tom and Sandy were his true guardians, committed to and interested in him and in his future without **reservation**, obligation or regulation. He didn't need to worry anymore about what Stewart or anyone else would have to say. It no longer concerned him.

"Hi, Stew, this is Billy."

The voice on the other side was silent.

"What's the matter? Too much for you?" he continued playfully.

"Where have you been, Snick? Two weeks, and the whole world thinks you've been kidnapped. Didn't you hear the news?" Stewart was in a state of semi-shock.

"No, what happened? World War III?" Billy's thoughts were clearly on the same wavelength as Tom's and Sandy's.

"The cops are looking for you, and there's a reward for your return. You hit big time. And even Herman confessed that he 'rolled' you with some friends. Is that true?"

"I guess so, but that's in the past. I'm doing really well now and I've got a real future waiting for me." Billy's voice was so full of **optimism** that Stewart paused to catch his breath.

"I don't get it. Where've you been? I thought you were dead, and now it sounds like you're cruisin'. What's the scoop, man?"

"Oh, I've just been hanging out with friends, staying out of trouble and keeping busy. How have my folks taken it?"

"They're worried out of their minds, what do you think? Snick, I can't believe I'm really talking to you. I mean, you sound so happy, and I couldn't even get to sleep a couple of nights worrying about you." Stewart paused once again, totally confused from the nature of the casual voice on the other side. "If this weren't so serious, I'd think you were playing a joke on everyone. But it's been two weeks. Where are you?"

"Oh, I really don't know, but I think it's somewhere between Earth and paradise. I think I'm on a small island. Yeah, that's it. I'm on a small island, and it's really great here. A lot of freedom, a lot of peace."

"Hey, don't give me some fairy tale crap, Snick," Stewart **interjected, perturbed**. "You and your peace and freedom talk. What, are you on drugs or something?"

"Whoa, don't put me down, Stew. I'm doing real fine, and I'm not on drugs like most of our friends. They're the ones who are all screwed up, and that's because they don't know what they're doing or who they are. The whole world's on the eve of destruction, just headed for a one-way trip to total **annihilation**."

"To what? I don't know what you're talking about, Snick."

"Yeah, I guess you don't," Billy added in a somewhat philosophical tone. "I guess that's why I had to get away from the rest of the world. Nobody really seems to know what's happening, and so I had to find out for myself."

"Billy," Stewart pleaded, "come back home. I don't know what you're trying to say, but we miss you and I don't want to lose you. You're the best friend I've got, and now I can't even figure out what you're saying. Please come back. Don't drop out."

Billy hesitated, realizing that he had already made his decision the day he took to the streets, and even Stewart's words of desperation couldn't change his mind. His imagination was planning for the future, while Stewart's reminders were but yesterday's **discarded** news.

"Stew, I've gotta go now. Too much to do. But you'll hear from me again. So keep me posted on what's been happening. I'll check back with you in a week or so." Billy added one final comment, however, clearing the air of misunderstanding that Stewart might have had regarding his social involvement. "But remember, Stew, I'm not 'dropping out.' You can be sure that you'll hear from me, and so will a lot of others. I'm not 'dropping out,' I can promise you that. Okay, Stew?"

Stewart mumbled a few words indicating that he understood what Billy had said, but the words weren't important. The conversation was over, and Billy had alerted the outside world that they would be hearing from him. He was ready to begin his **quest** for the truth and to serve as **apostle** to **proselytize** the world to a **globally** spiritual rebirth of social awareness. He was the chosen one **delegated** with the mission of enlightening all people to the **impending peril** should they choose to remain ignorant to the actual threat of human extinction.

As he hung up the phone, Billy sang the group's **portentous jeremiad** to himself: "But you tell me, over and over and over again, my friend, that you don't believe we're on the eve of destruction." It was now up to Tom and Sandy and him to tell the world. Billy's friends, his parents, everyone would have to wait before he would communicate with them again. Even Stewart had nothing of value to say to him. Only gossip and rumors. But Tom and Sandy offered more. They offered purpose, direction and the means to achieve the goals they sought. He was indeed living on his tiny island paradise, but he was not alone.

CHAPTER XIV
Growing Up

When Tom and Sandy returned, Billy was anxious to know how he could begin to help them spread the 'word.' They had, however, already prepared for the next step. Tom carried in two brown paper bags filled with cans of spray paint, while Sandy brought in a bag of groceries and a smaller bag **teeming** with felt pens. They had **amassed** quite an **artillery**, ranging from thin pens of **pastel** shades up through the heavyweights, massive thick black felt pens **expressly** made for large block-letter signs.

"Well, Snicky, what do you think of all this?" Tom asked wide-eyed as a child who had just opened his Christmas presents.

"I think they're...'groovy'...Isn't that the word you used to say for this?"

"'Fab' and 'gear' would also fit," Sandy added. "But you're on the right track, Billy. But what's *your* word for it?"

"Gee, Twink, I guess I'd say it's 'righteous' and 'bad' and 'massive.' Yeah, 'bad and massive,' that's what I'd say."

"Now that's what I like to hear," Sandy replied, "what *you* have to say, not what you've heard us say. What matters most in life is that you express your own feelings, your own words, not those you've heard someone say generations before your time. And that's what the whole world needs to do – start over and get everything said in their own words." Sandy was on a roll again. "Our leaders seem to think they can talk for all of us. And just because they think the bomb worked in '45 and just because we've been fighting wars for thousands of years, they seem to think it's okay to do it again and again – like history is forced to repeat itself. But who wrote the history books, Billy? Tell me that."

"I guess the people who were hired to," Billy replied, hoping it was the answer she was looking for.

"True, my sweet young man. But they're only historians, just people who dig up the past. And **documenting misguided** policies of the past is no **license** for us to repeat our mistakes in the future. But then again, everybody thinks that's what history is for. Like we've got no choice but to head for World War III."

"And they're all wrong," Tom continued the **didactically dynamic diatribe.** "The **Establishment** thinks we'll all listen and obey, but we didn't in *Viet Nam* and we'll never **accede** to the government's wishes to destroy human lives like they did in *Hiroshima* and *Nagasaki.* It's time the political system owns up to its **reprehensible** conduct and stops blaming the rest of the world for its own **corruption** and **incompetence.**"

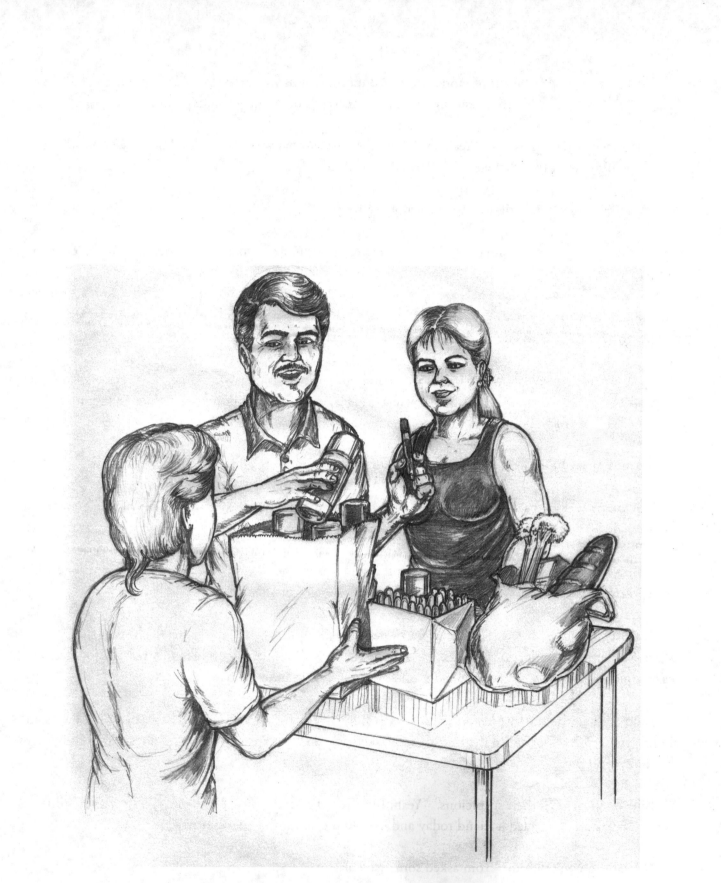

They had amassed quite an artillery...

Sandy **intervened** in behalf of **moderation**. "But don't get us wrong, Billy. We're not talking bad about America. We're just trying to defend the human rights that our country stands so much for."

Billy picked up on the idea. "Yeah, and everyone tells us what we've gotta do. Like in school, where we can't even argue with the teachers. Who says they're always right?"

"Who says they're *ever* right?" Tom asked **assertively**.

"Right!" Billy was **assimilating** into the conversation and the social rebelliousness of his **collusive compatriots**. "Why do we always have to listen to them and obey them? Why can't we write the rules the way we see the world? Teachers are twenty years behind the times. They think we should read a book, but I know that nobody likes to read when they can see the movie instead, and there's more to learn on a computer than there is in any stupid book about yesterday's news."

"You've really been getting into our movement, huh Snicker?" Sandy was **exuberant** about his attraction to their **enterprise**. "I think I love you. You're a one-in-a-million." And then she turned to a more serious subject. "Tell us, Billy, how come you ran away from home? You did, didn't you?"

"Yeah, I guess I did." Billy **mused** over where to begin, but Tom added his own theory first.

"We didn't think you were a typical street-person," he began, "not the way you talked and certainly not the way you got into those books and our ideas. For a guy who says 'nobody likes to read,' you sure seem to be the exception. You've gotten into some of those magazines like they were written for you. You ran away for a reason, and I swear it seems to me that the reason you did is the same reason we're doing what we're doing."

Tom's explanation saved Billy the need to get into too much detail about his **exploits**. They weren't asking for names and addresses, and he felt relieved to know they understood his inner reasons for escaping, **reassuring** himself as well that they had no interest to return him to his parents.

Sandy added the final words on the matter. "Billy Steele, right? I thought that was you. We've heard about you on the radio and in the newspapers. I didn't even bother to check the pictures. And Tom knew the reason you ran."

Billy confirmed all their suspicions. "Yeah, I had to get away because I was stuck in a **rut** and I couldn't seem to break free. I called a friend today and he told me about the TV reports."

"What did you tell him?" Tom asked somewhat alarmed.

"Nothing, Tommy, really nothing. I ran out of things to say. He just seemed to be part of the old problem, so I just told him that I'm fine and he'd hear from me again one day. Was that okay to say?" Billy was prepared to be lectured on "saying too much," but Sandy replied differently.

"Snicker, you have the right to say whatever you feel is best and nobody can condemn you for it. Nobody. I'm proud of you, and I know Tom is, too." She looked at Tom, who **concurred** by nodding positively though uncertainly. Sandy then continued, "So whenever you want to call your friend, or whenever you want to go back home, you just let us know. Or you can just do it without telling us, if you prefer. Don't let us stop you from doing anything you want. How does that sound, Snicker?"

Billy rested back against the couch. "You're two of the best friends I've ever known. I wish you were my parents. You'd be the best parents a boy could ever have."

"That's okay, Snicker," Sandy said. "If I were your mother, I couldn't fall in love with you. So maybe it's best the way it is." She then leaned over and planted another **passionate** kiss upon his lips, Tom meanwhile pretending to ignore the **blatantly exhibitionistic** event.

Billy reacted **blushingly** with a boyish grin, "Gee, Sandy, not in front of Tommy. How do you think he feels?"

"Like a brother," Sandy replied. "And how do you feel, huh Snicker?"

"Pretty good, Twinks. Pretty damned good." And with that, he reached his arms around her and **initiated** a kiss of his very own, one which he would never have dreamed of presenting to any girl he'd ever known before, but one which seemed to fit the occasion so perfectly that any other reaction would have been inadequate or out of place.

Billy was growing up in a hurry, and he liked how it felt.

CHAPTER XV
Decisions

The following week passed quickly, Billy **keenly** observing while Tom and Sandy mapped out strategies for their artwork and their methods for remaining undetected. Their goal was to add two 'messages' per week in Waikiki, selecting **remote** but visible spots such as on the third or fourth floor outside-walls of parking structures, where passersby could see the words during the day, yet few people would witness them being written in the evening hours.

Billy also needed to take some precautions. For starters, Sandy shaved off his wavy surfer-blond hair, **queue** and all, and he began to spend afternoons out in the sun, picking up a golden-brown tan under the always-intense Hawaiian rays. Tom and Sandy also bought for him a complete wardrobe of assorted clothes, including *Levis 501* button-fly jeans, assorted *Jimmy 'Z* shirts, and even a complete three-piece suit. Where they got the money Billy couldn't guess, but since they had low **overhead** and lived a **parsimonious** existence despite being so **staunchly resolute** in their mission, he **conjectured** that the two must have **scrimped** and saved a tidy sum along the way. And now they were spending some of it on their **prime** investment: the youngster himself.

Billy knew it was just a matter of days before he would be out in the streets, speaking to the world in **cryptic** fashion. He spent the week soaking up a tan while writing out his own **prolific** variations of scripture. "Don't follow the death train" was his first composition, followed by more creative expressions: "Land of the free, home of the stupid," "Where will your children live?" and "Prisoners don't ask questions." But then Tom and Sandy began to show their **prodigy** the art of fine writing, minimizing the words but maximizing the effect. **Honing** his skills, Billy produced some of his finest **pithy epigrams** before the week was through. "Where do we go from here?" was his longest, though it left the interpretation effectively **ambiguous** and thought-provoking. He then generated a **barrage** of smaller, more **laconic** scripts: "Go home," "America needs you," "Why worry?" "Stand up," "It's not true." They all contained **vast** treasures of hidden interpretations without appearing **garish** or **offensive**. The **artful** approach was to **forge** phrases that sounded innocent enough but yet would make the readers ask themselves "Why?"

Tom and Sandy tried not to influence Billy's style of thinking, choosing instead to allow him full **discretion** and support his every move. The discoveries he made were by reviewing his own art and analyzing its strengths and weaknesses. The three would discuss the nature of the so-called 'scripture-writing' **notion**, then Billy would reconsider whether his scripts fit effectively and appropriately into the **counterculture** concept. He had never before been given the **latitude** to direct himself, to decide for himself what was appropriate and what wasn't, and to learn by his own mistakes without having someone else point them out to him and make him feel foolish or **woefully** inadequate. Tom and Sandy were ideal teachers, and Billy found himself inspired to want to learn more, more about their cause as well as about political affairs in general. When they brought him a history book, he found himself reading from beginning to end, observing the past as though it were an exciting movie **encapsulating** man's lifelong **endeavor** to find peace in the world but in which man failed miserably time and time again.

Sandy shaved off his wavy surfer-blond hair, queue and all...

During one afternoon lunchtime **confabulation**, Billy pursued the history lesson with Tom. "How come, Tommy, the world hasn't ever avoided being at war? I mean, in all of history it seems like the amount of years of peace are hardly worth mentioning."

"Something like thirty total years of world peace in five thousand years, right?" Tom replied **pedagogically**.

"Yeah, something like that. And the other four thousand years in one war or another. That's a pretty bad track-record, huh Tommy?"

"Well, what do you expect from a world that believes history repeats itself? If everyone believes it'll happen again, then it becomes what is termed a 'self-fulfilling **prophecy**.' In other words, if you believe it hard enough, it'll happen. You see it in school every day."

"What do you mean, Tommy?" Billy inquired.

"Teachers say that you're no good, right?"

Billy nodded **affirmatively**, deeply interested to hear more.

"Then do you think they ever change their mind? Doubt it, huh? They say you're stupid or lazy and they grade you just the way they want to, no matter what you do. Let's face it, in America the way you get ahead is by saying 'yes' and doing what everyone tells you to do. Am I right, Snick?" Billy stared sadly toward the ground, hiding the tears of frustration **welling** up in his eyes. Tom knew he had touched a sensitive nerve in his young listener.

"So where does that leave us?" he continued. "I'll tell you, Snick. It leaves us stuck having to listen to what people tell us, people so **sheepishly malleable** that they simply follow what the books tell them. But we should realize that books, though important **repositories** for man's knowledge through the ages, are not self-proclaimed **arbiters** of wisdom. The value is in **stimulating** our imagination, not **prescribing** or **dictating** absolute truths to us. And when you question why the world has to **subscribe** to such **apocryphal** truths, you've become one of the few, one of the chosen few capable of redirecting man's energy and helping shape a better future for our world rather than view its eventual destruction through others' ignorant **acquiescence**."

"Thanks, Tommy," Billy added as he continued looking toward the ground.

"Don't take it as a compliment, Snick. It's a responsibility. You may be Sandy's 'Knight in Shining Armor,' but I see you as a *Robin Hood*, a person who has a lot of work to do and not much to go with. One day, you'll need to recruit others to help keep our messages alive. I don't think you'll ever feel like just settling down and living a normal, boring, ignorant life. I don't see it. You wouldn't have done what you did if you were content." Tom then paused a moment. "Are you content, Billy?"

"No, I guess not," Billy replied **solemnly**.

"Why not?" Tom further inquired.

"I don't know," Billy added uncertainly. "I guess because I'm not sure where I'm headed."

"Are you afraid?"

"No...well, yeah, I guess I am a little. I just don't know what's happening to me. I'm trying to figure it out, but I don't know. Nobody's ever asked me how I feel, not until I met you and Sandy. I don't know..." Billy leaned back against his chair and rested his folded hands atop the dining table. Everything seemed so confusing, so complex, when all he really wanted was a little freedom to live a simple, teenager's life. Had he made a mistake when he ran away? Was this what he really wanted? His thoughts ran **tempestuously** out of control; his wild, curious imagination was now being challenged by **counteracting** thoughts of doubt and regret, removing much of the thrill of the search. The freedom to choose a path remained, but the **sobering** uncertainty of his **plight** seemed to remove the magic, the exploratory excitement. Growing up wasn't all that much fun. In fact, it didn't seem like fun at all.

Tom knew that his young **protégé** was in a state of **bewilderment** and tried to **unmuddle** some of the **complexities**. "Does it hurt to leave your friends behind, Snick?" he asked **inquisitively**.

Billy leaned forward and rested his head on the table top. "Yeah, I guess so."

"Do you want to go back?"

"I don't know." Billy's voice began to crack, as he fought back the tears of confusion. "I don't know what I want to do, Tommy."

"There's one thing you've got, Billy. You've got the freedom to return anytime you want. I won't stop you from exercising your own **prerogative**. You can go back right now, back to being a regular, happy-go-lucky teenage boy. But once you go back, you can never return here. It just doesn't work that way. You see, we'd have you back but the rest of the world wouldn't go for it. Your parents wouldn't, the police wouldn't. Let's face it, we're the only real democracy. It's right here in this house. It isn't out there. America isn't the 'land of the free.' No place on this earth is free. Freedom comes from within, from inside your own soul. Your imagination is free, Billy. And that's why you have to decide your own future. I can't do it for you. And neither can your friends, your parents. Nobody. Do you know what I'm trying to say, Billy?"

"Yeah, I guess." Billy looked up at Tommy, the tears no longer trickling down his cheeks.

"Then I guess I'll let you think it over, Snick. It's your decision and I think you're old enough to know what's best for you. If you want to leave, don't let me know. Just go, and remember that you've got my blessing, mine and Sandy's, whatever you decide to do. You'll always be a special person in our lives. But you've got to follow your own dreams. Listen to your dreams, Billy." And with those final words, Tom stood up and walked slowly out the kitchen with his hands in his pockets, trying not to show any emotion.

The decision was Billy's. No one was telling him what to do. But now he wished someone was. It was a lot easier living like that.

The sun shone brightly outside as Billy **immersed** himself in deepest thought. There was no simple answer, not as simple as sitting outside and getting a suntan. No decision would allow him to just cruise for the rest of his life. Either way, he had a future ahead of him. But which one did he want to pursue: the normal, secure route or a bumpy, uncertain one? His thoughts flashed back upon his own family eating breakfast, their hurried silence, their **tacit hostility**. He knew why he had run away and he knew he had more running to do before he would find what was right for him. He couldn't return, not right now. It would make no sense.

The birds chirped happily outside, and Billy strolled out to join them under the refreshing rays of the sun. It was indeed a beautiful Hawaiian afternoon. As he rested **tranquilly** on a lounge-chair, Billy reflected over what had been said, soon drifting off in sweet **repose**. The afternoon nap offered no dreams but instead a welcome time-out from decision-making for the dream-**weary** traveler. It would soon be time to take bold action, but for now Billy was content to let the afternoon pass by without any further **cataclysmic** commotion. He wanted Sandy to come home.

CHAPTER XVI
Staking A Direction

"Hi, Snicker," Sandy called out cheerfully as she walked outside in her bathing suit to join Billy, who had already soaked up a healthy tan during his restful **slumber**. An hour had passed since Tom and he had concluded the **provocative** discussion and Sandy, informed by Tom of the **gist** of the conversation, was joyously relieved seeing Billy lying comfortably in the backyard, sensing that he had decided to stay.

"So what's new with you today?" she asked **probingly** as she lay on the lounge-chair next to her young **devotee**.

"Oh, not a whole bunch, Twinks. Just doing some thinking and some baking. Mostly baking." Billy felt very much at ease with Sandy around. She let him say anything without contradicting or even questioning him. He had her under a hypnotic spell, an **enthrallment** that only an innocent prince could cast upon another.

Sandy gazed at him in wonderment. "You're so satisfied and so confident. I can't believe you're only thirteen. And I really can't believe how much you've matured in the past three weeks. You remember how scared you were when I first found you?"

"No, not really," Billy replied, grinning shyly. "I was so stoned that I probably was more confused than scared."

"But tell me, Snick, why did you leave your parents?" Sandy asked in an **interrogating** curiosity.

Billy sensed that she was perhaps more interested in his future plans and whether the conversation with Tom had changed his **resolve** in any way. "Well, Twinks, I needed to leave. And I don't think I've changed my mind. I still need to find myself and I won't find it by returning now. Maybe someday, maybe never. But all I know is that I left because I wasn't needed there. And I think I'm really lucky that I found you. Or that you found me."

"That we found each other," Sandy added with sigh of **reassured** relief.

"Right," Billy replied as he nodded slowly. "And there's a lot for us to do. You and Tom and me. I really want to share in it and be a part of it. And I think it'll be a lot of fun, too."

"Billy, it's not all fun. It can be dangerous." Sandy lost her smile as she continued. "You're playing against the cops, against anyone who recognizes you, and against yourself."

Billy looked at her, confused. "What do you mean, 'against myself'?"

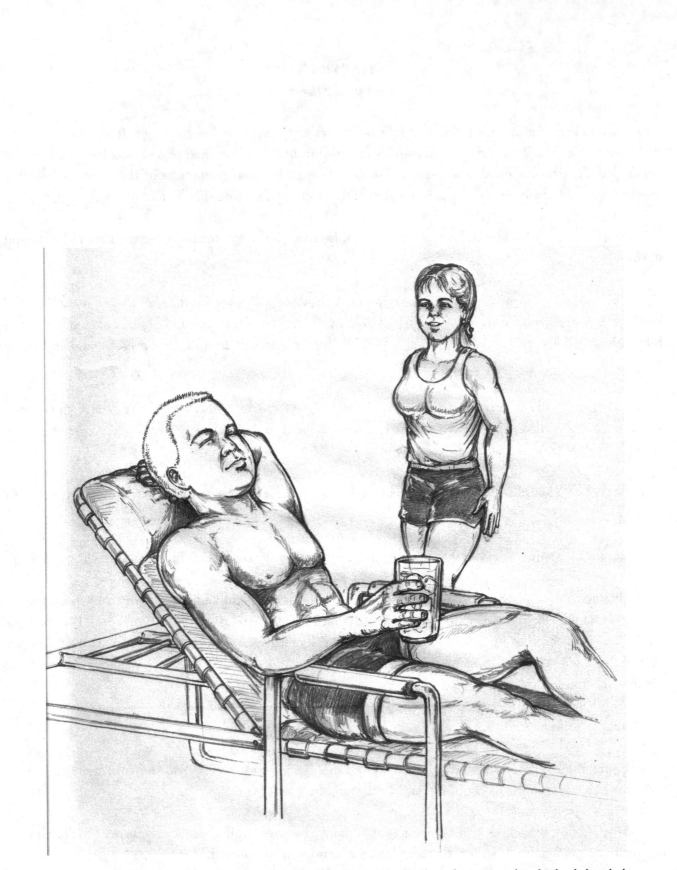

Sandy was joyously relieved at seeing Billy lying comfortably in the backyard, sensing that he had decided to stay.

"I think I understand kids like you, Snick. You're looking to express yourself, but you also want everyone to know who you are. You're an ideal candidate for getting yourself caught. But pay **heed**; once you get caught you can't continue. Not with us and probably not even on your own. You'll wind up with a record and you'll be back home, unless you get shoved into a **juvenile** facility."

Billy was quiet. The thrill of being 'big time' never carried with it an awareness of the risk of being stuck in prison or having an arrest record for the rest of his life.

"So before you decide to do this, you better know what it's really all about. It's not fun and games, Snick. It's 'criminal property damage,' something that nobody wants to do for kicks. Not unless they know how not to get caught. And, my young friend, this isn't **foolproof**. We can't guarantee a perfect job. You have to assume the responsibility, 'cause we won't be able to help you out if you do something stupid, or even if you get unlucky."

Billy grasped the **qualified** explanation of support. The mission was risky and **replete** with **manifold** obstacles, and just as in *Mission Impossible* no one would assist if he were to get caught. It was a **clandestine** operation, with all identities kept **mum**. And in keeping with **cloak-and-dagger convention**, the preservation of the group and the cause far outweighed the significance of any **lone** individual, including Billy. But although he was **blatantly admonished** about his **vulnerability**, he nevertheless was grateful that Sandy had so willingly offered the whole truth to him rather than have him commit his efforts without being **apprised** of potential **pitfalls** and attendant **repercussions** related to the **enterprise**.

"Thanks, Twinks. I really appreciate your telling me where I stand in all this. It makes me want to do it more. I'm ready to help you guys out. Just tell me when and where."

Sandy was hoping for this response and was prepared for it. "Okay Snick, you start tonight. You're officially one of the chosen few, and it all starts behind the *Hotel Honolulu* at 11:00 p.m. You pick the 'script' from the ones you've written this week. Just tell me which pens you want and we'll turn you loose. You know, we're only a few minutes away by bus, and you can walk back in half an hour after you've finished. How does it all sound?"

"Sounds like I'm in the 'big time.' But don't worry, Twinks, I don't plan on getting caught." Billy seemed certain of his abilities.

Sandy wasn't nearly as confident. "Just be careful. You came to us as a sudden, unexpected guiding light and I don't want to see you leave us quite so quickly. I'd rather you stay around a few days or weeks or years. Get what I mean?"

Billy understood. Whether she was referring to his commitment to the cause or whether she simply had a crush on him and didn't want to lose him, it didn't really matter to Billy. In either case she cared for him, and he was not about to **sever** this friendship because of some childish desire to become a foolish **martyr** to front-page publicity. A smart, **low-key**, undiscovered hero seemed more appealing to him, especially when he had a **fair maiden** awaiting his safe return.

"Don't worry about me, my delicious Twinkie. I'll be around for a while. I've got a lot of growing up to do, and I don't plan to do it alone. I guess you're stuck with me. "

Sandy giggled girlishly and then rested her face down upon the lounge-chair, letting the sun's rays warm and tan her delicate backside. Billy looked up at her, examining the soft and **supple contours** of her upper torso – where she had unlaced her bra – **marveling** at this mature adult who seemed to find in Billy something special that others apparently didn't fully appreciate. Maybe it was his youthful innocence or his **unbounded** ambition. But whatever it was, Billy felt like an **errant** knight about to prove his **fealty** to his **esteemed** queen. The evening would offer the first test of his abilities, and Billy grew impatient for it to arrive.

CHAPTER XVII
Being Prepared

As the evening approached, the moment of **initiation** grew more exciting for the three. Billy was **arrayed** in his *Benetton* pants and *Gotcha* shirt, a **subdued** dark-blue matching set, along with blue high-top basketball shoes covering blue-striped socks. He would blend in perfectly with the night – even his blue eyes would contribute to the one-color **motif**.

Preparations were made and carefully reviewed. Billy would take the 9:30 p.m. bus headed for Waikiki, then walk directly to the hotel, through the lobby and up the stairs. There were no security locks in the building, no keys needed to enter the stairwell. It was – as were most hotels in Waikiki – open-access, unlike most of the condominiums and residential high-rises. This was a typical tourist-hotel, like most of the taller buildings in the downtown Waikiki area.

Once in the stairwell, Billy would wait thirty minutes, then proceed to the fourth-floor parking structure, where he would use his deep-blue *Magnum-54* marker to etch his 'message': "Wake up and Listen!" It would hopefully be the beginning of a long-running series of messages, words which might eventually stir up enough interest to have all the tourists below talking about the **cryptic apocalypse**. The **mammoth** letters would stand out a full eighteen inches high and two inches thick, written in bold print, facing the streets of Waikiki. It would be days, perhaps even weeks before the State could **dispatch** a crew to remove or paint over the lettering, and the quality of the ink would resist fading and **weathering**. The message would remain **intact** for months if left exposed, and in the meantime there would be more messages to come.

Billy looked at his watch. One more hour and he'd be on his way. Tom and Sandy chatted with him, offering words of encouragement as well as words of caution.

"Work quickly," Tom suggested.

"Don't worry, Tom," Sandy **interposed** in the young man's behalf. "Snick knows what he's doing. He'll get the job done, and we can celebrate tomorrow by walking through and seeing how good it looks."

"Just be careful," Tom added, somewhat irritated at Sandy's overconfidence. "One mistake and it's over. Remember that, Billy."

"Don't worry, Tommy," Billy answered. "I used to 'tag' in school and I never got caught."

"Tagging isn't the same thing," Tom replied seriously. "That's just a ten-second job. This will take you at least ten minutes, if you make a professional piece out of it. You've got a lot of time and a lot of work. Half a job isn't worth a **plug nickel**. It's all or nothing. Every letter needs to be clear and correct. You don't get a second chance. No spelling errors, no slip-ups, and for God's sake don't fall off the railing."

"Don't worry, Tommy, I used to 'tag' in school and I never got caught."

Billy **dwelt** upon these final words of warning. It wasn't as easy as just signing one's tag-name on a garbage can. It would indeed be for him a time-consuming and **precarious** mission leaning over the parking structure and writing, almost upside down, upon the outside wall. Every letter, every stroke would need to be produced in a **meticulous** manner. His letters would all need to be properly **juxtaposed** and **aligned**. The 'p' might easily become a 'b' if he were to lose his **bearings** momentarily and accidentally **invert** it; there was so little room for error. Billy now knew the true significance of the expression 'letter perfect.' It wasn't a **trite** expression; it was an accurate description of absolute professionalism. He would need to make each letter, each pen-stroke, every **nuance** carefully **crafted**, just as though he were a *Renoir* or a *Monet* adding the final touches to a masterpiece. No **shoddy** slip-ups allowed. Everything had to be 'letter perfect.'

Time passed quickly, Billy returning to the living room to practice his artwork in a sketch-pad book, carefully measuring the size of each letter and double-checking to make sure they would all fit into the **allotted** space. The entire message would need to be centered, straight, and clear. He had no idea whether there might be a pipe or similar obstruction on the wall. If so, he'd need to **improvise** to get around the obstacle without affecting the quality of the message. There were so many **intangible variables**, but his **vivid** and **resourceful** imagination was prepared to handle whatever challenge came his way. The mission, with all its uncertainties, was **transmuting** into an assignment of **epic** proportions whose **crowning** achievement would prove a **milestone** in the young man's life. As the moment of truth neared, Billy could hardly sit still.

"Well, my hero," Sandy began at long last, "are you ready for the big battle?"

"No." Billy smiled, **peering** into Sandy's eyes, testing her reaction. But she didn't flinch, she didn't **deviate** from her **intransigent resolve**. She knew Billy well enough to sense his **palpably effervescent anticipatory zeal**.

"Well then, I guess we'll just have to find ourselves another 'Snick,' won't we?" Sandy replied in playful fashion.

Billy didn't want to pursue the game any further. He was too anxious to begin the adventure. "I guess you're stuck with me, Twinks. Do or die, it's me all the way." Billy stood up from the couch and gave the sketch-pad to Sandy. "Keep this in case I don't return," he added somewhat nervously.

Sandy's **sanguine demeanor** quickly changed to concern. "Don't talk that way, Snick. You'll do just fine. Don't worry. And if it looks too difficult, just quit and come back. You don't have to finish it tonight, you know."

Tom looked up from the newspaper he was reading, noticeably **nettled** by the **capitulatory** comment. "Don't talk like that, Sandy. He has a job to do and he needs to complete it. Don't go filling his head with half-cocked **notions** about quitting. We never quit, so let's not start talking that way now. Get my point?"

Sandy **glowered** at Tom who, newspaper in hand, stood up and stomped **irately** out of the dining room and into the kitchen.

"Don't worry about him, Snick. He's just as excitedly nervous as you and I are. You just do your best, and that's all we can hope for. Okay?" Sandy extended her hand towards Billy, who took it in his and held it tightly.

"Thanks, Twinks. I'll do a good job. You and Tom will be proud of me. I promise." And with those final words of **bravado**, the young warrior headed for the front door, a small brown paper bag in one hand. He was fully equipped, prepared to do battle against the elements. His heart was pounding wildly; he was about to make his **entrée** into society in a most unusual way. At long last the world was going to hear from Billy Steele. The cause wasn't really his own but the words were, and he knew that somehow somebody would know who the secret scriptwriter really was. If anyone would know, it would surely be Stewart.

CHAPTER XVIII
The Ultimate Expression

The Number-Nine Waikiki bus rolled along right on time and Billy hopped aboard, taking his seat near the rear of the half-filled vehicle. He sat **inconspicuously** on the window side, gazing at the glass and admiring his reflection. His hair was shorter than he could ever before remember, appearing more like a young tourist than a local boy. With his semi-formal **attire**, one would surely assume that he was about to go to a teen-disco or a **fancy** party, not **engage** upon **subversive** activities. His **upstanding** appearance was the perfect cover for his **villainous machinations**; no one even bothered to make conversation with the **juvenile miscreant**.

As the bus approached Waikiki, Billy's heart began to flutter and his pulse race wildly. He wanted to shout to everyone on board what he was about to do, or at least **confide** in someone who he really was and what he had planned for the evening. If only a friend of his were on the bus, Billy could **vaunt** his **elite emissary engagement** with **flamboyant ostentation**. But after his moment of **unconstrained aspiration** he quickly regained his composure and reminded himself instead of the **caveat** Tom had **impressed** upon him. It was surely not child's play, and he knew that professional **self-possession** was a must in this business. He rested back against the seat, counting down the moments and hoping the bus wouldn't stop at every corner.

After what seemed a **millennium** he arrived at the far side of Waikiki, where the hotels lay in abundance. This point would mark his departure from the bus and onto the streets for a **fugitive** moment. Billy stepped out from the rear exit and caught a glimpse he hadn't seen for nearly a month. The *Video Factory* was merely a stone's throw away, but Billy knew he would not have the opportunity to go there, perhaps not for a long time yet to come. He had to worry about the police, about being recognized by friends, and about completing his task as planned.

Within a block stood the *Hotel Honolulu,* a spacious twenty-eight-story building which included several floors for parking. The lobby opened up directly into the busy sidewalks of Waikiki, and as usual there were swarms of tourists walking to and from the building. He would enter unnoticed, unless by chance the security guards were on the prowl. There were so many factors he could not second-guess, so many **variables** which could **foil** the plan from the **outset**. But Tom and Sandy had accurately discovered that the access way from the ground floor to the fourth floor was **unhampered** by locks or keys. Anyone could proceed up the stairwell, and Billy soon found himself entering the building.

The hotel stairs seemed **vaguely** familiar to Billy who, **ascending** a couple of flights and resting between the third and fourth floors, attempted to **recollect** when he had been there before. It soon dawned on him that Sandy had found him on the rooftop of the *Hotel Honolulu*, and they had exited through these same stairs. Sandy had obviously been **scrutinizing** the **sizable** structure on the day she found him on the roof. And now, three weeks later, it was his turn to handle matters at the hotel, for the cause.

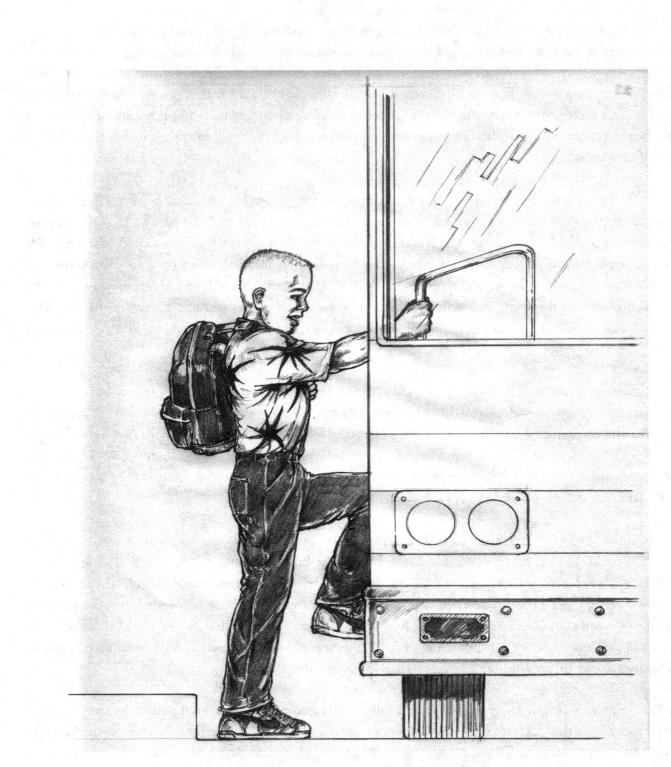

The Number-Nine Waikiki bus rolled along right on time...

The half-hour wait passed quickly, only a handful of tourists walking up or down the stairs. Billy meanwhile rested back and pretended to be asleep on a step, nobody saying anything as they walked by. Nobody noticed, and for one brief moment Billy felt relieved that people didn't care. This was the one time he didn't want another person to try to **befriend** him. When the last waiting minute **elapsed**, Billy calmly climbed the final few steps which led to the parking structure on the fourth floor.

The atmosphere suddenly changed. The floor was almost totally dark – most of the fluorescent lightbulbs were missing. It seemed peculiar to Billy that this floor would be so dark while the others were lit so brightly. But Sandy and Tom had planned every detail with **painstaking** precision, including the lighting. Billy began to **rummage** excitedly through his paper bag, pulling out his prized possession: the magnificent *Magnum* marker with the broad one-inch felt tip. It was brand new and would print clear, bold blue letters that would blend in with the darkness and go unnoticed, yet come to **resplendent** life the next morning.

The project was soon under way. Letters slowly appeared one by one in perfect **symmetry**, Billy demonstrating his **dexterity** and **sophisticated** tagging abilities in this more-advanced state of art. Within twenty minutes, stage one of the mission was accomplished. Not one car had driven by, but even if one had, Billy would have been able to quickly hide behind those already parked there. With the lights out, he could easily see any approaching vehicle, and with the generally incurious nature of people in Waikiki he doubted whether anyone would have cared if they saw what he was doing. He wondered for a moment if they would even notice the writing the next day. But at this moment it really didn't concern him. Now, his job was to make Tom and Sandy proud by producing a **lustrous** work of youthful art, and whether or not it would be front-page headlines the next day didn't matter all that much to him. He would be happy just to show his two **mentors** that he was capable of succeeding in this adult task.

Billy replaced the pen into his bag and pulled out his deep-green *Mean Streak*. He hadn't planned on adding any **frills**, but the temptation was just too overwhelming. He had an urge to color in the letters and turn them into a work of **multifarious** magic. He began his **embellishment** by adding a three-dimensional touch to the lettering, then adding crowns to the letter-tops and, using his red *SG-7* marker, **embroidering** the sides with **fanciful** cloud-like forms. It was no longer just a message; it was a painting. He had **transformed** the wall into an **aesthetically exquisite** mural.

When a couple of headlights beamed by, the young *Picasso* crouched down and pretended to be sleeping. The artwork wasn't visible from within the parking structure itself, so Billy felt safe knowing that no one could catch him **red-handed** alongside the graffiti. It was facing the other way.

Fifty minutes passed before Billy had completed the **majestic** masterpiece. As he looked down, finally, to view his **prodigious** project he noticed a small group of people looking up, silently admiring the painting. One had even brought out a camera and was taking pictures. The thrill of being the center of attention **whetted** his untapped imagination. Billy Steele, world famous painter, was now exhibiting his breathtaking murals in Waikiki for all to see. Tourists from all over the world would soon come to take pictures of his **ornate** artwork. There was fame and fortune awaiting him any day now. The feeling of **grandeur** brought a **euphoric** rush to his senses that only a sneeze could have accomplished before. He felt weak-kneed as he realized he was a star now. He was the center of the picture.

But then a **convulsion** of **consternation** raced through his body. A picture of him next to the graffiti he had made? That was **tantamount** to being caught in the act. He froze for a moment, paralyzed in his tracks, staring directly into the camera below. As the flashbulb snapped, the **uncircumspect stripling inadvertently** became the center of yet another **incriminating** photo.

Billy regained his senses, **precipitately** grabbed his bag and **bolted** from the wall, running at top speed down the stairwell, out the lobby and onto the sidewalk, turning immediately toward the back of the hotel and fleeing into the dark side-streets. He didn't bother to see if anyone recognized him. He was only interested in escaping from the scene and rushing back to the security of Sandy and Tom. The evening had turned into a **problematic** nightmare.

Tourists from all over the world would soon come to take pictures of his ornate artwork.

CHAPTER XIX
The Aftermath

It was after midnight when Billy arrived at the house. The porch light of the small wooden structure was on and he could see Tom and Sandy sitting at the dining table, **conversing**. They seemed **engrossed** in their discussion, neither bothering to look out the window to see when he was returning.

As Billy neared the porch, Sandy perceived his presence and jumped up excitedly. Tom followed slowly behind her, equally eager to see how things had **transpired**.

"Snick, I was worried to death," Sandy said in an anxious tone. "Thank goodness you made it back safely." She escorted him into the house, her arms around his shoulders as though she hadn't seen him in years. "Well, Tom, how does our boy look to you? And look at his face!"

Billy **scampered** to the bathroom to view himself in the mirror as Sandy giggled good-naturedly. His face was marked with a green slash running from his nose down to his chin. In the midst of fleeing the scene he had apparently brushed the pen across his face while hurrying it into his paper bag. He looked at himself with **chagrin**, shamed by his amateur appearance. But Sandy removed the humiliation with her words of encouragement.

"You look like a warrior who just won the battle. You did get it done, right, Chief?"

Billy felt braver. "Yeah, I sure did. It wasn't easy, but I got it done." He wasn't prepared to **divulge** the entire story, surely not the final terrifying and exposing moments.

Tom **probed** for additional details. "How long did you take with the lettering? I'd have figured thirty minutes max."

"Well, Tommy, I made the letters a bit more visible, so it took awhile longer. More like an hour." Billy's artistic **ardor** reemerged as he began to feel pride for his masterpiece once more.

"Any problems?" Tom inquired as though sensing the **inevitable** failures that most teenagers **encounter** when **undertaking** an adult task.

"Nope, everything went smooth as silk." Billy was **unflinching**, determined not to show any signs of fear or guilt. He had succeeded, and if anyone wanted to take his picture they could have it. The scripture was written, and that was his **primary** goal. "No problems at all, Tommy," Billy concluded and then flopped down upon the sofa. "Boy am I tired. Have you got anything to grind on? My feet are sore, and so is my body." He looked at Sandy, who smiled supportively, realizing that Billy was trying to act as **macho** as could **befit** him on this evening of unparalleled triumph.

"Snicker, you're a true hero," she added, "and whatever you want, just ask." Sandy then **ogled** him in her **coquettish**, **beguiling** way, adding "You're the boss."

Tom had heard enough. "Go on, get him something to eat. He's only thirteen, not twenty-three. Save your **cavorting** for the weekend. Right now, let's just call it a night and see how his message looks tomorrow. Good night, Snick," Tom concluded, "and congratulations on a job well done." He patted Billy on the shoulder and then left the room for the evening.

Sandy stayed behind for another moment. "Remember – whatever you want, Snicker." And then she went into the kitchen to prepare him a chicken pot pie.

The climax of the evening now passed, Billy removed his blue high-top shoes and **doffed** his *Gotcha* shirt, tossing it onto the dining table. There was time to pause and reflect, but his excitement during the evening left his energy sapped and he found himself instead barely able to keep awake, much less able to recall and **savor** the events of the day.

When Sandy returned ten minutes later with the heated pie, Billy was already fast asleep atop the sofa, his legs **splayed** and his head propped up against the side cushion. The activities of the day had concluded for young Billy Steele.

"Sleep well, angel. You can eat this another day," she whispered. Sandy then slipped a kiss upon his cheek, but without a reaction from Billy she knew he was **oblivious** to her remark. He had done a man's job, but his young teenage body and inexperienced teenage mind showed the wear and tear. If he were an adult, she would have been able to share in his delight. But for the teenager, sleep was his real need, and though she felt somewhat abandoned and deprived of her moment of **exultation** and **uninhibited** celebration, Sandy knew she would have to accept Billy's limitations. He still had much growing up to do, and to do so too quickly would simply **undermine** his youthful innocence. She had to respect him. After all, it was his **premature** escape from his own parents that landed him **serendipitously** in their hemisphere, and Sandy knew that any unfamiliar or threateningly **presumptuous** act might just as easily **rekindle** his urge to flee.

CHAPTER XX
Returning To The Island

Billy returned to his dream island, but the scene had changed. It was a larger island more **densely** overgrown with trees and shrubs as well as more **pronounced** in its **topographic relief**. The beach was not as sandy, nor as inviting. The shoreline resembled the coastline of Makapuu Point on the East Shore, rocky ledges **jutting** out to the sea. The surf crashed with more violence than before, and he felt more scared than isolated, more in fear of his **welfare** than **entranced** by the **solitary** spectacle. Nature was not his friend in this variation of his favorite dream. Even the weather itself was more cloudy than sunny. The winds picked up, and he found himself **longing** to escape to another dream.

As he walked in his dream up one of the island's moderately sloped hills, Billy turned to see, behind him in the distance, several people **clad** in strangely-colored **attire**, carrying what appeared to be spears. Though fully half a mile away, they approached rapidly towards him. Billy could sense they were not friendly. Had he trespassed on their island, or were they **encroaching** upon his territory? Were this the same island as before, he would have indeed claimed it rightfully as his own, but this was most certainly not the same land as in his earlier visions. He had apparently mistakenly landed upon someone else's dream-island, and now he feared for his life.

The dream soon became an **unbridled** nightmare, the warriors getting ever-closer while he, in his short-cut jeans and bare chest, fought hard to stay ahead of them. The underbrush dug into his bare feet and tore away at his body, and he could feel trickles of blood oozing from his side, down his legs. As he neared the **summit** of the hill, he could hear **distinct** voices behind. They were advancing closer with every passing step he took. He accelerated to a full run up the hill, stepping **heedlessly** on razor-sharp **spires** while being mercilessly **lacerated** by the taller shrubbery and its thorn-like branches.

At last Billy reached the top, but what he saw left him in **petrified paralysis**. Below him, one hundred feet straight down, lay an ocean whose **beckoning** waves crashed fiercely and **unremittingly** against the jagged coastline. He was standing atop a **precipitous promontory**; there was nowhere further to run.

As he turned to witness firsthand the identity of the savage **stalkers**, he **discerned** the figures of five or six people, each one **arrayed** in a headband of different color. The **pernicious predators** were indeed carrying spears and were focused on one person as their **quarry**. He tried desperately to **distinguish** the identity of the **baleful** band, but before they got close enough for Billy to **distinguish** and **differentiate** the warriors under the makeup and headbands, his attention became firmly fixed upon one member, the leader whose spear was lifted and pointed directly at him.

"I thought I might find you here one day, sonny boy," the warrior chief said with a **wry**, **sinister** grin. He then hurled the spear through the air, headed directly at Billy. It torpedoed itself quickly closer, Billy's eyes bulging as he could see it approach inch by inch, ready to tear his flesh open as he watched helplessly. Closer and closer. Twenty feet. Ten feet. Five feet.

... people clad in strangely-colored attire, carrying what appeared to be spears ... approached rapidly

Billy jumped up, screaming and sweating. His eyes were open wide and he noticed it was early dawn. But the birds were silent. There were no morning sounds. He turned his head to reach to the table for his shirt, when he noticed a hand resting against the side of the sofa. Without looking up further, he slumped back against the cushion, glassy-eyed and in **mortal** terror. Whoever the hand belonged to, Billy did not want to know. The nightmare had left his senses totally bare and **shell-shocked**, and now the alien hand's appearance so soon after his moment of dream-destruction could not be **confronted**. The dream had been too shockingly real, and in his **frayed** state even the sight of his numb **appendage** appeared as a **fey portent** of **impending perdition**. He dearly wanted to seek **refuge** under the covers but had not even a shirt to hide in atop the sofa. All he could do was close his eyes and pray for the hand to be just another **illusion**, another bad dream.

Two hours later Billy awoke, fully **cognizant** of the dream he had experienced and the hand he had seen. He turned his head slowly, fearing that the five-fingered **specter** would still be there. But it wasn't. He was alone in the morning hours, alone to **ponder** what the dream and the hand had meant. It was all so real, yet all so fantastic. He felt like a fly in a spider's web, unable to **alter** the course of a **destiny** of the worst of all possible hells. It was a feeling he had never before experienced, a helplessness that he never thought could **vanquish** and **subdue** his sense of **infallible autonomy**. All his **exploits**, all his accomplishments had brought him to this dream, this **utter** denial of everything he had ever achieved. Why did he feel so **pathetically** powerless after all he had done the night before?

Billy sat himself up on the sofa, trying to understand why his conscience wouldn't let him **savor** his independence. The minutes ticked by, but he remained **unnerved** and unable to **console** himself.

"Good morning Snick," Sandy whispered from the doorway. "You're up early today. Planning on coming with us to Waikiki?"

"No, Sandy," Billy responded, **rigidly postured** and looking at her somewhat dazed. "That's okay. I think I'll stay here and just relax. I'm kinda tired. Maybe I'll just watch some TV." The words came out lifelessly and mechanically.

"Okay, but you'll be missing the fun of seeing what you created. Tom and I will be leaving in a short while, just in case you might change your mind." Sandy was still in her evening robe, an attractively green silk garment which made her look more **matronly** and **dignified** than when she wore jeans or tight slacks. But nothing looked very appealing to Billy at the moment; all he wanted was to be able to just go back to sleep, to forget about the warriors and the hand.

"Go without me, please," Billy **implored**.

Sandy shrugged her shoulders and turned to go back to her bedroom. "Okay, if that's what you want." She seemed somewhat **ruffled** by his disinterest to go and his **indifferent** attitude toward her enthusiasm, but suspecting that Billy had obviously woken up on the wrong side of the bed she didn't seek to further the **discourse**, exiting quietly instead.

Once Sandy was out of sight, Billy got up and walked to the bathroom towards the medicine cabinet to withdraw a few sleeping pills. The **incapacitating** feeling of **insuperable impotence** and inadequacy left him **bereft** of his characteristic **vim** and **vitality**, and he knew only the **sedative** effect of a **soporific** drug could **palliate** the **debilitating** and **subjugating disquietude** he had been **stricken** with. Perhaps he would awaken more refreshed at a later hour. As he **ingested** the pills with a glass of water, he reflected upon the artwork he had created. Was it worth the effort? What would it accomplish? Did his dream have something to do with the drawing?

Before he could ask himself any more questions, his eyelids began to close rapidly. He had only enough time to slip into his shirt and drop heavily onto the sofa before fading again into unconsciousness. The sleep he sought had arrived, and now he wished only to be spared having any more dreams. He might not survive another one.

CHAPTER XXI
The Reaction

A loud bang brought Billy out of his deep sleep. The garbage men were emptying the trash, throwing the metal cans back upon the sidewalk. The banging first sounded like gunshots, until he realized where the noises were **emanating** from. Nonetheless, he had been disturbed from his peace, and he knew he would not be able to get back to sleep. It was already past nine, Sandy and Tom having long since left the house to survey the work he had done the night before.

Billy stood up **groggily**, pushing himself off the couch, then bending over to touch his toes and regain consciousness from the deep sleep the pills had produced. He did not remember dreaming any further, and even though he had only slept for a few hours under the power of the tranquilizers, he felt newly refreshed and no longer affected by the dream that had haunted him earlier.

Lifting himself up after his wake-up exercise, he **espied** the telephone, his communication with the outside world. Should he call Stewart? Maybe the two could share in the happenings over the past couple of weeks. He **yearned** to make contact with his closest friend, to begin to patch up the distance that had developed as a result of his decision to run away. He hadn't recently been able to communicate with boys his own age and could feel many of the sources of youthful **diversion** fading, as though his adult **confreres** were **compelling** him to abandon his childhood dreams and apply himself toward more mature and **concrete** goals. The grown-up words of encouragement and praise did little to satisfy his **adolescent** desire to run out into the streets with his skateboard and cruise around, pursuing **unpretentiously puerile** pleasures.

Billy had spent three weeks cooped up in an adult world, and besides the few attempts to look **macho** or act like an adult, he felt totally out of place. He was as deprived here as he was at home, only now he had lost touch with his lifelong friends. His parents didn't even seem as restrictive anymore, for in their company he always had **unfettered** access to school and his friends as well as weekend liberties at the beach.

Some **nebulous inquietude** had affected him three weeks ago, producing in him the desire to run, but was it something his parents had said, something his teachers had said or perhaps just a buildup of **irrepressible wanderlust** that **impelled** him to try something new, something different? Had the **credulous lad** simply been **hoodwinked** and **bamboozled** by **spurious** and **mendacious** stories of **salvation** from his **peers**? Stewart had never encouraged him to run away; Butch was the one who claimed that the streets offered a better life. But where was Butch now? If he had believed his own **specious** words, wouldn't Butch have been the first to follow this **hortatory** advice and flee?

Billy's imagination wandered as he searched for a clear answer. He recalled Tom's words which echoed deep within his soul – "We're the only real democracy…it's right here in this house" – and knew the freedom he was enjoying with the two was indeed **virtually** unlimited, without **dictatorial** demands or **stultifying** restrictions. He could never enjoy similar freedom at home. But did he really want to have so much freedom? The **dilemma** weighed heavily on his mind, so he turned on the television to try to relax and reduce the **anxiety**. He wouldn't decide anything further today. But the questions nevertheless haunted his efforts for **tranquillity**.

Tom and Sandy arrived back at the house around noon, midway through an old episode of *Married With Children*. They seemed excited, so Billy got up and shut the TV off, awaiting their comments.

"Well, Snick, you really did it," Sandy exclaimed proudly as she walked through the front door carrying a bag of groceries.

"Yeah, it really looks good," Tom added as he followed behind her into the kitchen.

"Gee, I'm glad you liked it," Billy responded, his **disposition** somewhat brightened by the words of praise.

"What gave you the idea of all the colors, Snick?" Tom asked from the other room. "Looks like we're going to get far more exposure than we bargained for." He seemed satisfied, but Billy detected a tone of disapproval beneath the personal **plaudits**.

"Do you think I overdid it, Tommy?" Billy asked, hoping to **ferret** out the source of the apparent irritation.

"Well, Snick, maybe a little." Tom walked out of the kitchen and into the living room, where Billy was standing. "It could affect our next move. I think everyone on the island will be reading your message, and it means there'll be a swarm of cops looking out for a follow-up. I mean, you really did it big!" Tom's last words were filled with a pride which indicated that his overall impression of Billy's activities was favorable. "Yeah, I'd say we've gotten our point across. Now I've got to figure what to do next."

"Why not just keep going as planned?" Billy asked **naïvely**.

"My young man," Sandy said as she carried out some fruits on a tray, "this is going to hit the papers and maybe even the newscasts. You gave Waikiki a new look, and I think all the hotels in town are going to toughen up on security to prevent a follow-up." Sandy also seemed unusually proud of the event, as though Billy had done something they had never been able to accomplish by themselves.

"Does that mean I get an 'A'?" Billy asked in an attempt to **infuse** some youthful **leavening** into the conversation.

"Maybe more like being Number One on the most-wanted graffiti list," Tom replied in **earnest**.

The reply was not what Billy had wanted to hear. Rather than turn the activity into a mischievous **caper**, his adult companions were **sobering** him up to the true nature of the crime. It wasn't a 'kid's' game anymore, and Billy felt a **pang** of fear once again overcome him. The more he **collaborated** with his senior associates, the more he **longed wistfully** for the company of friends his own age. This was not becoming his vision of freedom; it seemed more like a course headed straight for prison.

CHAPTER XXII
Viewing The Results

The next day represented Billy's last chance to catch a glimpse of his **polychromatic** message before the weekend arrived. Once Friday passed and the weekend approached, Billy knew that many of his friends would be in Waikiki, and he couldn't risk being discovered. Weekday school-hours were the perfect time for him to go with his **surrogate** parents, pretending to be tourists. Billy's hair was still **conservatively** short, and having dyed it slowly for the past week the color had changed from a slightly-dirty-blond to a dark brown with shades of red. The **subtle**, **masterful** disguise **transformed** the **artful dodger** so perfectly that he would **gawk** at the sight of himself in the mirror whenever he went into the bathroom. "Sharp, really sharp" was his self-analysis, the only words that seemed to come from his lips whenever he would see himself through the looking-glass.

As Friday arrived, Sandy elected to chaperon the **neophyte** to Waikiki. They left together, taking the 10:00 a.m. bus to survey the **aesthetically enhanced epigrammatic advisement**. Sandy wore her youthful pink jeans coupled with a loose-fitting *Generra* shirt, while Billy decked himself out in a striped *Italian Boys* shirt matched with a pair of import-pants. Sandy particularly liked the combination. "You look like Jim Morrison," she said as they rode the bus together. "Ever heard of him, Snick?"

"No," Billy replied, confused. "Who is he?"

"Well, he's not around anymore, but when he was he was the sexiest singer anywhere. He made Mick Jagger look like a schoolboy."

"You mean, like a wimp?" Billy inquired seriously.

"Well," Sandy continued somewhat defensively, "Mick Jagger's not a wimp, Snick. He was and still is one sexy man. I tell you, when he sang 'I can't get no satisfaction,' I didn't believe a word. He could get anything and anyone he wanted. But that's not the point. I was talking about Jim Morrison, not Mick Jagger."

By now Billy was totally **bewildered**, being compared with someone who was sexier than a wimp. The association didn't make sense to him, and Billy didn't know whether to take it as a compliment or a **snide** remark.

Sandy didn't **belabor** the **analogy**, either. Instead, she just rested back on her seat and let the bus take the duo to Waikiki. She realized that she and Billy were worlds apart. But they did share one thing, one priceless **attribute** which Billy possessed naturally and which Sandy sought to **retain cosmetically**: youth. And by being with Billy – sharing in his lifestyle and his hopes and dreams – she felt she could best hold onto the fibers that keep people young. For her, Billy was more than a young friend. He was her key to preserving her own youth. And though her attempted flattery didn't produce any communicative understanding, she knew she could offer Billy many other treasures that

Sandy elected to chaperon the neophyte to Waikiki.

he might **pine** for, whether today or in the not-too-distant future. After all, she was years older and more experienced than he was, and what she knew she could teach to him. She knew Billy was an **avid** and devoted **disciple**.

The two sat on the bus in silence, Sandy **speculating** what her **unsung** hero must have been thinking but unaware that Billy's thoughts were on Stewart and his other school friends. The two were far away from one another in thought, but they were headed towards something in which each had a significant stake.

When the bus turned onto the main street, Billy and Sandy grew increasingly restless and excited at the nearness of the **culmination** of their **collaborative** efforts.

"Does it really look 'rad,' Twinks?" Billy asked shyly.

"'Rad' is a pretty good word for it. Yeah, I'd say more like 'awesome,' but 'rad' is one way to describe it. You wait, it's just a couple of streets away. Let's get off here so we can walk to it." Sandy **nudged** Billy's arm, **discreetly** directing him to get up to exit at the next opportunity. "Ready for the grand opening special showing, Snick?"

Billy nodded, and the two prepared to depart at the next bus stop.

The afternoon was invitingly warm and sunny, the sidewalks **teeming** with tourists **clad** in bright-colored swim shorts and bikinis. It was always easy to **distinguish** the tourists from the local residents: The visitors wore only the loudest and most **vibrant** color fabrics, whereas the more **subdued** local folks chose not to look 'like a tourist.' Each group had its own style, though the tourists never perceived just how **curious** they looked. To them, everybody dressed alike. Of course, they didn't realize they were comparing themselves with other tourists. It was a local 'inside' joke. In Billy's own school, the students would **deride** those who wore **fancy**, loud clothes. The usual comment would be "How's it going, Mr. Tourist?", though occasionally it would be **embellished** with **hostility** – **disparaging epithets laced** with **acrimonious aspersions** regarding how the boy or girl was acting like a tourist, behaving as though he or she owned the island. It was certainly not a compliment to 'look like a tourist,' and as a result Billy had never before **incorporated** such **modish** styles into his everyday apparel.

But with Tom and Sandy, Billy was offered an entirely new identity, one **replete** with his own **fancy** wardrobe and a new image to match. With the necessity for anonymity, the clothes **befitting** an island visitor were a **prerequisite**. But Billy's pride was also **bolstered** at the same time, as he now began to look upon himself as a **luminary** for whom only the best clothes would **suffice**. He was no longer the 'typical schoolkid' in **drab** clothing. He had **transformed** himself into a **dignified** young man – **albeit** a tourist in appearance – and now appreciated his newly acquired expressive **attire**.

After the two **alighted** from the bus, Sandy led Billy, hand in hand, in the direction of the *Hotel Honolulu*. The warmth of such **intimate** contact was a thrilling experience for the **callow**, **ingenuous** teenager who had not held another's hand since the Summer Sock-Hop, when Darlene Johnson asked him to dance to a slow ballad. Her hands, however, were cold and lifeless, and the dance was more an **obligatory concession** than the **emergence** of a new romantic fling. Billy's past experience with kissing another girl was comparably unspectacular; when he kissed Becky at school during recess, they surely didn't go holding hands afterwards. For the couple, the act of kissing was no more than an exploration, a time to discover whether someone else's mouth offered a different taste, a new thrill. But there was nothing special about it, certainly nothing as explosive as the kisses he had recently shared with Sandy.

And now, walking down the street holding her hand, Billy felt a strange satisfaction, as though he were holding his mother's hand and his girlfriend's hand at the same time. His mother hadn't held his hand since he was nine, at which time she told him "You're old enough to walk yourself across the street. It's about time you begin to grow up and take your own responsibility." Four years later Billy had **decamped** from the nest, and yet even in his new-found freedom he missed being treated like someone special, like the child he still **yearned** to be.

Sandy helped fill this **void**, and as the two strolled casually along the store-fronts Billy was eternally grateful for the opportunity to once again play the role of child, happy and carefree under the **aegis** of his **benevolent** protector. Sandy, on the other hand, looked upon the event from a different perspective. For her, the **intimacy** revived memories of her own youth, when she walked along the store-fronts in Laguna Beach holding on tightly to her boyfriend, Ben. The two shared in everything they did, from writing on the walls to joining in the **sit-ins** and protest-rallies, eventually running away from home together and joining a **commune** on the outskirts of Los Angeles. There was so much to share – from *Viet Nam* to *LSD*, from long hair and **psychedelic** glasses to strolls on the beach and throwing frisbees.

But times changed, and as the era of the hippies and *Viet Nam* faded into history Ben grew **weary** of the drug scene and decided to pursue a more **conventional** career and lifestyle. The day he asked Sandy to marry him, their relationship ended. The **conformity** associated with marriage symbolized for Sandy total individual surrender to the 'system,' a word she **detested** and to which she would never **accede**. Ben eventually became a banker, and Sandy found herself totally **estranged** from him within a year.

Tom became her **salvation** four years later, in 1976. During the bi-centennial celebration in San Francisco, she saw him for the first time. She had traveled to the 'flower city' to experience firsthand the **stimulating** sensation of the streets **renowned** for their 1960s **legacy** of free love and **counterculture communal coexistence**. Ten hours by bus landed her right in the middle of Market Street, a short walk away from Haight and Ashbury Streets, the most famous intersection during the acid-era '60s. The streets were magical for her. They were the birthplace of the *Jefferson Airplane* and the *Grateful Dead*, of all the magical memories that Scott McKenzie later **encapsulated** in his anthem:

"If you're going to San Francisco,
Be sure to wear some flowers in your hair;
If you come to San Francisco,
Summertime will be a love-in there."

The **incendiary** impact of the **subversive** streets reenlivened in her a sense of activism, an urge to **extol** the virtues of freethinking by speaking out against the **mediocrity** that had **befallen** her life and had sucked Ben into the world of **capitalism**. Tom was in the middle of the bi-centennial rally, holding a sign that read "200 Years Closer to the End." The words were **enigmatic**; her **visceral** response was "Why?"

Tom answered her in a low voice, one of confidence and experience. "Because that's where we're headed. Right over the edge."

From those first few words, Sandy knew she had found in Tom the voice she had seen **suppressed** in Ben. Tom was a **dissenter**, one of the chosen few still able to **retain** an individual identity and personal voice amid all the **propaganda** of "U.S.A. means 'Peace.'"

The two became **kindred spirits** from that moment forth, planning one rally after another and joining in **sit-ins** wherever they could be found. For **sustenance**, they labored **sedulously** at odd jobs, inspired by nights filled with music of *Peter Paul & Mary*, *Joan Baez* and *Bob Dylan*. On one **auspicious** evening they managed to attend a concert featuring *Pete Seger*, whose rendition of *Turn! Turn! Turn!* energized in them the desire of doing more than simply join others in their activism. They would devote themselves to their own cause, their own private **crusade** to make the world take note of man's apparent **ineluctable** doom.

Within ten months they had **masterminded** dozens of graffiti-messages – which they later **euphemistically** termed 'scriptures,' later shortened to 'scripts.' Their words were decorated on all the garbage cans and all the porch steps throughout downtown San Francisco. But with **notoriety** came risk. Those who knew of their **exploits** were initially supportive, but after a while Tom and Sandy sensed from their friends a growing disapproval of their **audacious** activities, which had become well known to the police as well. Then one summer afternoon as the decade of the '70s drew to a close, the two decided that the '60s movement was **defunct** in San Francisco, that their so-called supporters had grown **weary** of the causes they had earlier **championed**. For everyone else, *Viet Nam* was now but an unpleasant memory and Nixon a faded footnote of the *Watergate* era. Tom and Sandy **hibernated** awhile but then began a renewed mission, a **renaissance** of their activities.

In 1983, the two **peripatetic** protestors took their pens and their savings on the road, visiting small towns and large cities, finding few people interested in what they had to say. In **rural** areas, few were there to read the messages; in **urban** and **metropolitan** regions, on the other hand, graffiti was so **rampant** that their **mordant** messages were camouflaged amongst the **surfeit** of meaningless

The streets were magical for her.

ubiquitous obscenities that seemed to **flourish** atop **virtually** every wall and building. There seemed no place left to make an impression.

Tom and Sandy discovered Hawaii in the late '80s when they saw an advertisement on the television, the announcer proclaiming proudly: "Hawaii, the last unspoiled frontier. Come join the thousands who flock daily to our shores, where **serenity abounds**." Tom's initial commentary-reaction was 'Where ignorance abounds,' that's what they should say." And from that remark Sandy lit the fuse, adding "Maybe we can wake up the people there, huh Thomas?"

Within two weeks they were in Hawaii, living in an affordable apartment at Waikiki, **scouring** the city for possible places to leave their messages. But they were also fully aware of the *Waikiki Police Station* situated one block from their beach-side room. They needed to move farther away to avoid being easily tracked to their residence.

A two-bedroom house fit the bill perfectly. Located just ten minutes by bus from Waikiki, it was the ideal location at a most reasonable rate. Their move to this new dwelling occurred six months later, after they had surveyed the island and had become acquainted with the lifestyles of the people, the generally **lackadaisical** nature of the police, and the watchful **omnipresence** of the hotel security guards. Because of the guards, any **covert** action they took would need to be carefully pre-planned. Tom was especially reluctant to jump into anything too quickly or without proper precautions; two months passed before he felt comfortable writing in Waikiki, still opposing targeting anything as obvious as hotel walls or street signs.

When Sandy had found Billy atop the *Hotel Honolulu*, she was in the process of determining whether rooftops would be suitable sites for the scriptures, but Billy added a new dimension to the plans. With his **daredevil** attitude and reckless **abandon**, **tempered** with some serious coaching, Billy could produce what Tom knew he could not do alone. Billy had the desire and the **naïveté** to perform splendidly without the least bit of **trepidation**.

Three weeks of guidance and preparation had led to the production of the semi-professional artwork left for all to see, and now – three long decades after her **rendezvous** with Ben – Sandy was finally sharing again in the same excitement. But she was now sharing it with Billy, not Tom. Billy reminded her of those magical days with Ben, times far more thrilling than those recently with Tom, whose adult **rationalization commingled** with **circumspect deliberation** was becoming a source of frustration and irritation for a girl who treasured youth and **spontaneity**.

Billy had been discovered just in time, just as Sandy and Tom were differing in everything they did. While Sandy wanted to further the cause, Tom seemed to always have an excuse why they should delay actions until a later time. His **dilatory demeanor** reminded Sandy of the change that affected Ben before he became totally removed from the activist lifestyle. Tom was becoming ineffective, afraid of taking the chances he **endorsed** in prior years. Even their once-**wanton** and **licentious** relationship had become **domesticated** to the point of dullness. Sandy suspected that he would soon ask her to marry him, which in her eyes would close the book on their association; she **dreaded** though silently anticipated the **fateful** words coming from Tom's lips.

The young man with her represented a new beginning. He wasn't assuming the role of her son because she didn't want to begin motherhood at her still-youthful age. Sandy knew that their relationship could blossom into more than simply between adult and child. She was counting on it.

The two held hands as they **traversed** the busy sidewalk, then came to a standstill when they reached the *Hotel Honolulu*. Neither Sandy nor Billy looked up at the wall, however. Instead, Sandy stared into Billy's eyes, smiling in her charming way. "Snick, are you ready to look up at what you've created?"

Billy gazed back slyly and flashed an **impish**, **pixie-like** grin. "Sure, Twinks, but kiss me first."

The temptingly **seductive** words left Sandy **dumbfounded**. "What, right here? There are a million people all around."

"So, they won't mind," Billy replied **coyly**. "Call it your gift to me underneath my masterpiece."

A couple stopped and stared as Sandy and Billy embraced one another in an **impassioned** kiss. The two were **steeped** in their own world, **oblivious** to and **divorced** from the tourists and locals who walked by chuckling and offering words of **unequivocal** encouragement. No one noticed the large lettering that stared down, not while the two **salacious** lovebirds rocked each other under the **sultry** Hawaiian sun.

At long last, the two looked up, admiring the **shimmering** green-and-blue mural of art that floated above like a cloud. It seemed more like a hotel-produced advertisement than a work of some graffiti-gang. The professionalism **belied** the true purpose of the message. The words had less impact than the **splendor** of the colors, but Sandy and Billy nevertheless saw it as the greatest achievement either had ever **engineered**.

Neither observer spoke a word. Between the **potency** of the kiss and the magnificence of the artwork, words seemed inappropriate. The two focused their attention upwards, attracting a crowd of people who stopped to also look up at the lettering. Everyone seemed to be hypnotized, Billy finally breaking the silent stares of **stupefaction**, refocusing his attention instead on a more personal note. "Gee, I hope Stewart sees this," he whispered to himself.

Sandy remained momentarily in a trance from what had **transpired** underneath the message-**mistletoe** but then just as quickly regained her composure, abruptly grabbing Billy's hand and **prodding** him to move with haste. The two walked hurriedly back to the bus stop, Sandy saying not a word. Billy looked at her, confused. Was she mad at him?

The bus rolled up, and the two boarded to go back home.

... *the two looked up, admiring the shimmering green-and-blue mural of art that floated above like a cloud.*

CHAPTER XXIII
Looking Back

On the route home, not a word was spoken. Sandy spent the entire bus ride staring out the window, with an expression closely resembling disappointment, almost as though an **ineffable** sadness had come over her. Billy wished to speak to her, but her **dour** and **detached countenance** alerted him to maintain his distance.

For Billy, the experience in Waikiki was thrilling – kissing a beautiful woman beneath his **grandiose, ostentatious** work of graffiti art. He had become the center of attention in all of Waikiki at that moment, everyone and everything around him in some way affected by his presence. The **resplendent** hotel wall bore **testimonial** to his **triumphal tryst**, and the sightseers were **vicariously vivified** through the spectacle he and Sandy put on for them. But he hadn't expected the **subdued** reaction that she had felt, and her **willful** isolation left an **uneasiness** within him. Was this sudden **reticence** due to something he had said or done, or perhaps something he had not said or not done? He knew that eventually she would say something to him, since he had not consciously **provoked** any anger or **hostility**; she couldn't be seriously angry with him. But her **disengaged indifference** left a cloud of uncertainty around even this **presumption**.

The two exited the bus and walked the final block home in **saturnine** silence. They were not holding hands anymore and seemed to be returning in quite the opposite mood felt earlier in the day. Something had obviously happened, but Billy didn't have the slightest clue what it was.

Tom greeted them as they entered the house. "Well, was it what you expected?" His voice wasn't **exuberant**, simply **inquisitive**.

"Yeah, Tommy," Billy replied, "it sure made the streets shine. I think it'll help us get our message out to everyone."

"How about you, Sandy?" Tom continued.

"Yes, it's a nice message. Very effective." Her voice was expressionless.

Tom sensed Sandy's lack of enthusiasm. "What's the matter, girl?" he asked **straightforwardly**. "Do you think he shouldn't have made it so colorful?"

"No, that's not it," she replied defensively. "It was fine, and you don't have to push your ideas on me. I know what you thought of it." Sandy was clearly disturbed about something Tom had said earlier, but Tom didn't want to **resurrect** the matter at this time.

"Okay, I get your message," Tom replied **curtly**. "Let's leave it, then. So it's a good message. I'm glad everyone's happy."

But it was clear to Billy that no one was happy. There appeared to have been a change of heart everywhere. Not only in Sandy, but also in Tom, and even in Sandy's attitude toward Tom. The **latent rancor** reminded Billy of his own parents, the mood signaling the **prelude** to a fight. The gun was loaded, and all that was needed now was a little further **antagonism** to spark **unbridled** warfare.

"What's the matter, Sandy?" Billy asked in a tone of concern. "Didn't you like what I did?"

"Yeah, Snicker, it was just fine. I just don't feel very good right now, that's all. But I'm proud of you, no matter what Tom has to say about it."

Tom began to respond in his own behalf but then stopped short before the words were released, remembering the **sagacious** old **saw** as **applicable** today as since time **immemorial**: Hell hath no **fury** as a woman scorned. He didn't wish to **precipitate** a **row** involving Sandy, not when she was in as **volatile** a temper as at this moment. He could **articulate** his observations and **reservations** at a later time, when cooler heads **prevailed**.

In the meanwhile, Sandy excused herself quietly and walked towards the front door.

"Do you want me to come along, Twinks?" Billy asked softly and **earnestly**, hoping to find out why she was feeling so unsettled.

"No, Billy, I think I just want to be alone for a while. I need to take a walk. But I'll be back, don't worry."

"Better let her go, Billy," Tom added in a **lordly air** of **defiant bravado** once she had left the room. "I know the way she is, and when she starts to act like that nothing will change her mood. She's a strange lady, always trying to be somebody else."

But Billy didn't understand what Tom meant and he wouldn't **elaborate**, merely adding **imperiously** "One day, you'll understand." To the young man, Tom's words sounded like those coming from his own parents, hiding from him the meanings and truths that were supposedly too 'adult' for him to understand. The exclusion angered him; the **mutual** respect was suddenly missing. Tom was now the holder of secrets, whereas Billy only wanted to be treated as an equal.

Tom retired to his den, leaving Billy alone in the living room to **ponder** everything that he understood and didn't understand. The painting was a success, or was it? Sandy seemed happy, but yet she obviously wasn't. Tom was satisfied, but yet he had said something to the contrary earlier. And Sandy's mood was "not for him to understand." There was so much that didn't make sense now. Billy wondered whether he would even be asked to produce another message. He could pose the question to Tom, but somehow he didn't think Tom would give him a straight answer. Instead, the **addled** orphan **opted** to turn on the television and simply relax on the couch.

An hour later, as three o'clock passed, nothing had been **resolved**. Sandy had not returned and

Tom was **immersed** in reading, into which he usually remained hours at a time. Billy knew that Stewart would be home by now, and he was dying to pick up the phone to make contact with his best friend.

Touching the receiver and dialing the number, Billy felt a strange peace enfold him. He had **plumbed** the depths of the outside world, had gained a freedom he had never before known, and yet out of it all he discovered what he had lost in the meantime. With the responsibility of being free came an **estrangement** from the life he had known so well throughout his life. Whether or not Tom and Sandy had any good words to say about institutional living, Billy knew that all his years of schooling, all his family structures, even his after-school baseball leagues and surf-meets contributed to making him feel a part of a larger society, part of the **stable** world around him. The freedom he was now experiencing, on the other hand, brought with it merely a **superficial** and **tenuous** purposefulness, one subject to disintegration at the slightest disturbance. Sandy and Tom had spent years creating their own cause and defining their own mission and purpose behind it all, and yet in one short afternoon a minor **squabble** had distanced the two from one another and from their cause, with nothing left to cling to. Without the cause, Sandy's life and Tom's life seemed valueless. But Billy's wasn't. He still had his friends, his family, his school, his way of living. Whether or not it all still existed for him wasn't clear, but his call to Stewart would help him clarify the state of affairs back in the real world.

"Hello, can I please speak to Stewart?" The mother was on the other line. "Yes, this is a friend of his." He hadn't tried to disguise his voice, but fortunately the mother hadn't suspected who he was, if she even cared. Billy sensed, however, that she did care yet simply wasn't aware who was calling. The family structure extended beyond his own immediate household, with other parents concerned, too – a **symbiosis** not found in Waikiki – **compassion** an **integral** element which families close to one another shared. Stewart's mother cared deeply for Billy but didn't know it was Billy Steele calling. He smiled as he **ruminated** the thought. His **vivid** imagination never seemed to slow down, always analyzing and **presupposing** how others were feeling. But his imagination could not assist him in analyzing Tom and Sandy, a couple torn between two worlds with apparently little hope for eventual **reconciliation**.

"Stewart, how's it going?" Billy was **ecstatic** to be able to talk with his friend.

"Billy, is that you?" Stewart replied in a whisper.

"Yes, of course. Who did you expect, Frankenstein?"

There was no sound from the other side of the line. Billy began to worry. "What's the matter? Something happen?" His thoughts spun wildly, **envisioning** his house burning down and his parents dying in the blaze.

"No, nothing's the matter," Stewart finally replied. "Just that I'm so surprised to hear from you. I swear, everyone thinks you died. The rumors have been flying around everywhere, and Sam

114

Herman has gotten the blame. Everyone thinks he gave you an overdose of drugs." Stewart was silent once again, collecting his thoughts amid the shock of discovering that his friend was still alive.

"Has anything changed? I mean, anything new?" Billy asked calmly and **nonchalantly**, hoping to exhibit an **insouciant impassivity**.

"Billy, where are you?" Although whispering, Stewart was almost at the **brink** of **hysteria**.

The lonesome wanderer began to feel **uneasy** and somewhat displeased at himself at having caused such **anxiety** in his closest friend. "I'm staying with some friends. I'm still in Hawaii, Stew. Don't worry about that."

"What do you want me to do, Billy? Can I help? Should I tell your parents? What's happening with you, Billy?"

Billy realized that the past few weeks were a nightmare for Stewart Simon, a person who seemed to care almost too much. Before, Billy would have considered **compassion** a **superfluous** sentiment, but now he **yearned** for such **empathy** and **fellowship** to **imbue** his life. Every expression of concern and caring was welcome, and Billy found himself apologizing for putting Stewart through what had apparently been a **torturous** month-long **ordeal**.

"I'm sorry, Stew. I didn't know that I'd be screwing you up by doing all this. Yeah, I want to go back. I really do. I really do." Billy hesitated and thought to himself for a moment. "Tell you what, Stew. You try to figure out some way for me to get back, anything that you can figure out. Then I'll call you back in a few days or so, and maybe by then we can decide what to do."

"Why not just come back? Why not just get away from where you're at and come here?" Stewart wasn't whispering anymore. "I'm sure my mom can explain it to your folks. And what should I do? Call your folks?"

"No, Stew, don't do that. It'll just mess them up and they'll blame you. Just hang loose and we'll think of something." Hearing the front doorknob being turned, Billy added hurriedly, "Gotta go now, but I'll call you back in a couple of days." The **wary waif** hung up the phone quickly; Sandy had returned. He had not even been able to ask whether Stewart had seen the scripture. But then again, it seemed the least **relevant** of subjects to discuss at the time. Billy's **picaresque peregrination** was becoming less and less attractive by the moment. It stood for nothing. Nobody was really interested, including those for whom the cause existed. The only one who liked it was Billy himself, and yet it didn't mean enough to even **warrant** mentioning to Stewart. After all, it wasn't anything more than words on a wall. How could that compare with friendship and belonging? Where was the purpose in writing **cryptic** messages? Did it really matter that people would stop and ask "Why?" They stopped when Billy was kissing Sandy, and that required less preparation and less risk. Of the two, Billy knew he'd rather have the opportunity to kiss Sandy again than spend an evening coloring walls.

"How are you feeling, Twinks?" Billy asked in a concerned tone.

"Better, thanks to you, Snick," Sandy replied, smiling. "You never seem to lose your good-naturedness. That's what's so special about being young. I envy you. But I won't try to compete with you."

Billy stared up at her, wondering whether this was another of those expressions that he was "too young to understand." But inasmuch as Tom **comported** himself with **aloof arrogance** – refusing to explain himself – Sandy on the other hand **elaborated** on her statement in a down-to-earth manner.

"What I mean, Billy, is that we all have a goal in life. Some people try to become rich and famous, while others just want to find some peace of mind. For me, it's always been the challenge of rebelling. I think that's what's kept me young and I think that will always keep me young. And you've helped bring that feeling back to me, something Tom hasn't been able to do for years. But I've got to be honest with you, Billy. I've taken advantage of you. Too many things I should have known better than to do."

"You haven't done anything wrong," Billy protested. "Not unless you did it while I was sleeping."

Sandy chuckled aloud. "No, that's not what I mean. See, you're such an innocent boy that you don't even know what I mean when I try to explain it to you. Look, let me put it into words that even a cute kid like you can understand."

Billy rested his head upon his palm, gazing up at her as though *Adonis* the teenage 'Thinker.' Sandy **peered** into his baby-blue eyes, realizing that she would have a difficult time explaining something serious to a lad who would rather just play around. "Okay, little brat, cut that out," she said playfully. "Do you want me to tell you or not?"

"Sure, that's why I'm listening," Billy replied, admiring her as though *Cupid* had landed an arrow dead-center into his heart. "I'm all ears." The satisfaction in having communicated with Stewart produced in Billy a **buoyant**, light-hearted feeling, knowing he no longer needed to take his present **predicament** quite so seriously. There were now **myriad** future options at his **disposal**.

"Okay, smart-aleck. Let me ask you something, okay?"

"Shoot..." Billy answered, changing his pose slightly by resting his head upon his other palm.

"Do you like me, Billy?" Sandy was serious.

Billy came to attention, resting back against the sofa. "Sure I do."

"How much?" Sandy pressed.

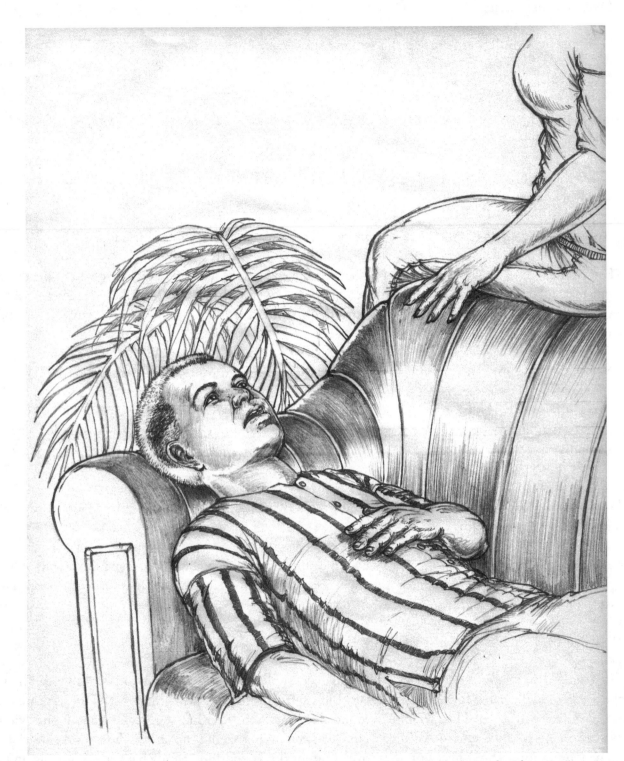

Billy stared up at her, wondering whether this was another of those expressions that he was "too young to understand."

"A lot, I guess." Billy was anxious to know where the questions were leading.

"Like a mother, perhaps?"

"Yeah, maybe." Billy wasn't sure if this was the answer she was seeking.

"Like a girlfriend, perhaps?"

Billy hesitated. "Well, maybe like an older sister, I guess. Yeah, or maybe an older girlfriend," he concluded, nodding his head up and down.

"That's the problem, Billy. I'm like your older sister, and I'm trying to act like a girlfriend who's your age. Get what I mean?"

"No, not really," he replied. "You're my friend. Does it matter what kind of friend?"

"For you, no. For me, yes. And that's what I found out today, in Waikiki. I love you a lot, but for different reasons than I should. I'm not fifteen anymore, but I keep trying to act like a teenager. And I began to think that you saw me as a fifteen-year-old girlfriend. Isn't that stupid?" Sandy paused to let Billy respond.

"No, that's not stupid. You're my friend, and anything you want to do, I'll do. Fair enough?"

"No, not fair at all. Not for you. And I should know better than to lead you on. I think it's time for us to stop pretending to be someone we're not. I think we should be friends, pure and simple. I'm not your sister, I'm not your mother, and I've got no right to pretend to be either. So let's just be friends, okay Billy?"

"Does that mean we can't kiss anymore?" Billy felt a **twinge** of sadness, faced with the loss of **reprising** his most thrilling moment since leaving home.

Sandy banged her fist against the wall. "Damn it, Billy, you make me feel so cheap. I'm trying to own up to my age, and then you throw in those innocent punk questions that make we want to go crazy. How do I say 'No' when I really want to say 'Yes'?"

Billy had the best answer. "Just say 'Yes.' That's easy, isn't it?"

"I swear, Snick, you are one helluva tough cookie to swallow." Sandy had obviously convinced herself to take a solid stand against further attraction to Billy, but within a minute he had totally **undermined** her defense. He seemed to have her wrapped around his finger, sensing what she really wanted and willing to give in to her childlike fantasies. He was indeed keeping her young, no matter how hard she tried to avoid the temptation. The conversation was over, but not the friendship. Sandy banged the wall again and walked towards her room. But before she was out of sight, she turned and smiled at Billy, whispering one last word. "Thanks." Then she was gone.

CHAPTER XXIV
The Altercation

Sandy never again raised the issue to Billy regarding their relationship. The following day she appeared uncharacteristically distant and concerned moreso about Tom's changing attitudes. The **disputatious** duo **wrangled** over **picayune** matters such as the quality of breakfast and whether it was going to rain – acting more like a married couple as the weekend developed – which reminded Billy of the family he had left behind. But although the problems at home centered around a lack of communication, the discussion here was more **acrimonious** and far less **conciliatory**. Billy preferred the less **antagonistic** atmosphere; he never enjoyed watching people yell at each other.

On Sunday, the two reached what appeared to be an **impasse**, a disagreement in **ideology** which showed no sign of compromise or **resolution**. The issue was Billy himself, and it erupted over dinner into a full-scale verbal **assault**.

"I think Billy's old enough to decide what to write next," Sandy told Tom just as Billy was preparing to sit down to eat.

"I didn't say he wasn't," Tom replied, "but I just think we've got to cut down the artwork and make the script shorter."

"What do you think, Billy?" Sandy asked in a polite but impersonal tone.

Tom interrupted the start of Billy's reply. "Does it really matter what he thinks? He's only a child."

"So you feel you can think for him, huh Thomas?" Sandy **retorted**.

"And you think he's a professional, do you, Sandra?" Tom added the formal **appellation** sarcastically. "Why, because you think he'd make a convenient boy-toy?"

Sandy was **outraged** and **infuriated**. "Don't throw your inadequacies on me just because you've forgotten how to be human. You and your **doctrinaire utopian dogmas** that *you* don't even follow anymore. Where are *your* pens? Where are *your* signs? All *you've* got left are books. Nobody ever changed the world by reading books. You're no *Gandhi*, I'll tell you that."

The **incendiary altercation** rapidly **intensifying**, Tom added **kindling** to the rising flame. "But at least I've still got ideas, not some **whim** about making a child some reflection of one's own **narcissism**."

"And what does that **jargon** mean?" Sandy asked angrily, slamming the palm of her hand against the dining table, the plates rattling.

119

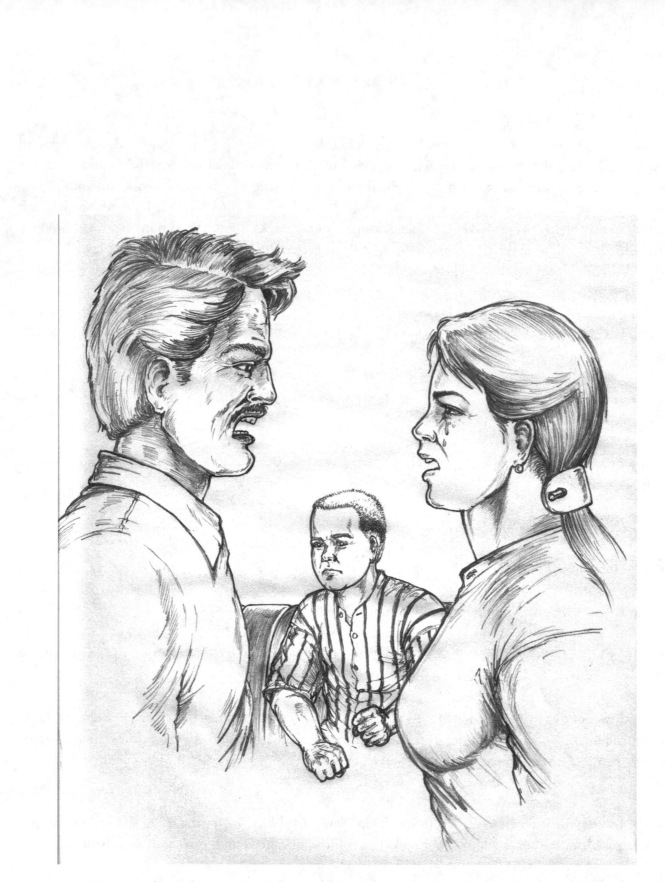

The incendiary altercation rapidly intensifying, Tom added kindling to the rising flame.

"What do you think? You seem to have all the answers. Why not ask your little Snicker?"

Billy tried to get a word in edgewise. "Maybe if we just talk about it —"

"Talk?" Sandy screamed. "That's Tom's specialty, talking until you don't know what he's saying. You know, Thomas, once you had some guts behind what you did. When you cared about your messages, you stood by what you said. But now you're nothing but twenty-four-letter words that say less and less about more and more. Nothing about everything, that's what I call it now. And when Billy finally says something, you put it down. When's the last time *you* ever wrote a message like that?" Sandy was **defying** Tom to defend himself, but he merely **eschewed** the **provocative** discussion.

"Time to eat. Your logic is **garbled** and typically **involuted** to excess. I should know better than to communicate with someone like you. You just twist and **distort** the words until they make no sense."

"Tom," Sandy concluded, "*you* don't make any sense anymore. That's what the problem is. And I don't see what ever kept me believing that you were still working for a cause. You lost it years ago and I just kept trying to hang on to it."

"Well, dear, let it go then. I'm not stopping you." Tom's words were determined and unemotional.

"You're not stopping anything anymore, and that's your real problem. For you, everyone can just get up and leave. You've never made an attachment to anyone or anything."

"That's right, Sandy. And that's what keeps me free. I haven't attached myself to anything. And neither have you."

"But that's where you're wrong, Tom, and that's where we totally disagree. I *have* attached myself. I attached myself to our cause, I attached myself to Billy, and I once attached myself to you." Her eyes started to well up with tears, but Tom's brutal reply turned them into angry daggers.

"Your mistake, not mine. I never asked you to follow me. You chose to, so don't put the blame on me."

The **vitriolic** argument had reached its **crescendo**. The communicative **friction** between the two had **escalated** to such a point that Billy could not see how these two had ever understood one another. Perhaps they never had, or perhaps their changing **perceptions** had pulled them apart. But whatever the case, it was clear from the buildup of **aggression** and frustration that an **inevitable rift** had formed between the two.

Sandy rose slowly and **deliberately** from the table and carried her half-filled dishes into the kitchen. She seemed outwardly calm, but Billy and Tom both knew that at any moment she might turn and throw the dishes, food and all, at either of the two. Tom kept one eye in her direction at all times, ready for any number of possible **retaliations** she might **summarily** and mercilessly launch. However, she merely marched to the kitchen, cleaned off the dishes, and then disappeared **unobtrusively** into her room.

"Don't try to figure out women," Tom said to Billy after Sandy was out of sight. "They change like the weather."

But Billy wasn't convinced that the change had come solely from Sandy. There was more to the widening of the **schism** than merely one person's moodiness. It always took two to **exacerbate** an existing **breach** in communicative understanding, though Billy knew better than to sound off with any sentiment of his own. There were enough **discordant** viewpoints floating around, and the last thing Billy wanted to do was have his own **convictions** further **degenerate** the **tenuous tranquillity** by putting Tom in high **dudgeon**.

As the night wore on, Billy heard nothing from either Tom or Sandy. Both spent the evening in their **respective** rooms while Billy lay on the sofa, his eyes closed, analyzing his own family problems and reflecting just how minor they seemed compared to the ones he had witnessed between his two guardians. His parents didn't speak at length to one another, but it was due moreso from boredom and its **attenuated** familiarity over the years than from **overt animus**. Billy had mistakenly **inferred** that his father's disinterest in meaningful **discourse belied** a more **sinister latent hostility**, but having witnessed firsthand the verbal **fisticuffs** exchanged today in all its **fury**, he more fully appreciated his parents' comparatively **innocuous plight**. All his family really needed was a fresh outlook on life and a renewed interest in one another. His mom surely didn't hate his dad, and his dad never raised his voice to the mom. It was just a matter of silence, a buildup that led the son to imagine the relationship on the **verge** of collapse. But as he sat back and meditated, Billy could not recall a single incident reflecting actual **adversarial** conflict. They shared in Billy's schoolwork, they worked equally hard to offer one another the best of everything – except conversation – and they never attacked one another's **rationale** or **ideologies** in order to **bolster** what they themselves believed in. And they certainly never spoke of regretting that they had ever met one another or that Billy had become part of their lives.

Billy opened his eyes as he rested, dwelling upon that final thought. "Mom and Dad never told me 'I wish you'd never been born.' They never ever said that to me. Not once." The shocking **revelation** brought tears to his eyes. "Damn it," he continued quietly to himself, "they never wanted to make me feel unwanted, and I ran away from them. Hell, what did I do it for?"

His early childhood memories raced through his mind: the times the family went to the beach together, saw the *Hawaii Islanders* baseball team play at *Aloha Stadium*, and traveled to *Castle Park* to ride the assorted Disneyland-like rides and practice batting in the baseball cages. And the gas-powered race-cars, they were so much fun. His dad would ride with him, and together they would try to run his mom off the road. It was all so exciting, a family outing with no afterthought of guilt or change of heart about having done it. The family stuck together through thick and thin. When he got hit by another person's surfboard, his parents visited him every day at *Queen's Medical Center*; when he had an appendicitis, they were with him every day and stayed as long as visiting hours permitted at *Kuakini Children's Hospital*. They never stopped supporting him with praise and confidence. Though they may have had less to say to each other, they never spared sharing their love with him. Perhaps this expression **vicariously** satisfied what they formerly gave to one another, before Billy was born. The love had been channeled through him, and yet he had chosen to run away from them.

The image of his parents alone, in **woeful desolation**, sent a shudder through his body. Without him, they had nothing left. He was their everything, and yet he had been **gulled** into believing that he was nothing. How had he allowed himself to become so **misguided** as to choose to follow such an **injudicious** path, **subscribing** to Butch's **threadbare** tale that all children are unwanted and must therefore escape to find a 'better life'?

Billy shook his head and then rested it in his hands. "Why did I listen to everyone else? I've screwed up everything and everybody. Even Stewart." The tears began to flow freely, but he didn't wish to stop them by discontinuing his train of thought. He needed to recognize the truth now that he was in the middle of the **crisis** involving Tom and Sandy. He needed to decide for himself what to do, and he knew that he could not depend on Tom, Sandy or anyone else anymore. He needed to **rely** upon himself. He was the only person who knew all the reasons behind his leaving home, and only he could determine the best course of action now, both for the benefit of those he loved and those who loved him.

123

He needed to decide for himself what to do...

124

CHAPTER XXV
Packing Up

The next morning, Sandy was packing her belongings. When Billy awoke on the living room sofa, he could see bags **strewn** about, each filled with clothing and **trinkets** accumulated over the years.

"What's happening?" Billy called out as he stretched his arms and adjusted his eyes to the bright sunlight. "Looks like you're moving." Once the words were out, Billy knew he had summed up the situation precisely. "Sandy?" he inquired in a tone of insecurity.

Sandy emerged from her room with a handful of assorted clothes, dressed in her green *Jordache* jeans and white pullover shirt. She was dressed to travel, Billy sensing it the moment he saw her.

"Hi, Snick. How's everything going with you this morning?" She appeared cheerful and **sprightly**, not angry and frustrated as she was the night before.

"I'm okay, Sandy, but what's happening? You planning on going?"

"Yeah, that's what I'm doing. Time to move on. Nothing more I can get out of this place. Like the song said, 'We'll sing in the sunshine.'"

Billy didn't follow the reference but knew she was firmly committed to leaving, for her own good. The decision wasn't hasty or **tentative**. It was a **calculated** and conscious move, one which she had no intention of changing.

"So, where does that leave Tom?" Billy questioned conversationally.

"Frankly, my dear boy, I don't really give a damn." The usually **trite** *Gone With the Wind* phrase possessed an **uncanny relevance** at this moment, **aptly** reflecting Sandy's **indifferent** attitude. She had tired of Tom's **languid** lifestyle and **feeble** excuses and felt no desire to continue, even for another day, headed away from her own chosen path.

"What about me, Sandy?" Billy ventured in a more concerned tone.

"For you, Snick, I really do 'give a damn.' I want you to come with me. I don't want you to be stuck here. It's a bad scene going nowhere." Sandy paused, then continued, summing up her latest **assessment** of the situation. "It's all falling apart, and I don't even think Tom's going to stick around. He'll probably bum out on the North Shore with some of his academic communist friends shooting the breeze about human inequalities for a few months and then go back to the mainland. I don't know. He'll probably become a banker. That would be so typical." Sandy had no lost love for Tom, Billy could tell, and the more she spoke of him the less flattering the words became.

125

"But where would we go?" Billy asked, searching out all the information available to him.

"Maybe to San Francisco or L.A. I think we could get something going there. You might even be able to get back to school and start to find yourself. What do you think?"

Sandy didn't know the real story behind Billy's running away. To her, Billy's personal **exodus** was **irreversible**, true for most runaways thrown out of the house by their parents. But Billy's situation was different, and he knew it. His parents never asked him to leave nor had they ever suggested that they might one day leave him behind. Besides Butch, only one or two distant friends ever suggested that he escape, and even then they brought the idea up merely as creative conversation. No one besides Billy really took it seriously; not even Stewart himself was certain why his closest friend was so **intent** on leaving.

"Well, maybe I better start packing too, huh Twinks?" Billy offered, knowing that he needed to leave the house no matter which direction he chose to travel. Over the past few weeks, he had managed to acquire a half dozen assorted matching outfits, three pairs of dress shoes, and numerous t-shirts and shorts. He had been well taken care of while he stayed with the two and felt a **pang** of regret seeing the couple dissolve their union so abruptly and **heatedly**. They really were nice people, only a **trifle** confused as to what they wanted out of life. Tom seemed to want to sit back and enjoy a normal lifestyle, but Sandy would not **conform**, continuing instead to reject such **notions**. Billy couldn't really side with either, since each had a chosen path worth pursuing. But he wondered why they hadn't communicated more openly when they first met. Perhaps this **rift** would never have developed had they known each other better in the beginning. But such was the fate of a relationship dedicated primarily to a cause. The cause became the **focal** point, but they never actually got to know one another. Everything was based on idealisms, without human interrelationship, and the end-result was an **irreparably divisive** quarrel over **ideological** differences.

His parents, on the other hand, began their lives together in openness, not based on some **chimerically quixotic** belief that they were going to **disabuse** and **redeem** everyone else in the world. Billy now realized that people can't change other people; satisfaction can come only from within one's own heart. He had sought to **effect** changes in others but had lost touch with his own inner feelings. In his **quest** he had overlooked all that he had and replaced these gains with all that he lacked. But in doing so he lost his most **cherished** possession: his family. This newly-recognized **revelation compelled** him to reevaluate his **appraisal** of his life at home. Billy now knew he had simply misunderstood his parents' intentions, blaming them for becoming distant from one another, when all along they had never begun to drift apart. Perhaps they were overlooking the value of communication, but they were surely not drifting apart. Billy belonged to a family, one in which the **primary** goal was to maintain **solidarity**, a togetherness of that precious family unit. Everything else was secondary. There was no **mystical** cause that could threaten the **familial** bond; only the absence of the members themselves could **jeopardize** the unit's **integrity**.

Billy folded his hands together and looked down in shame at the floor. When he had run away, he had taken away one of the most important **components** from the family. He denied his parents the one thing they had placed all future happiness in. How could the family survive without him? He was their true cause.

"Sandy?" Billy began, shaking and on the **verge** of tears, "I think I better go home. My mom's probably really worried by now."

Sandy looked up from her packing. "Snicker, I never heard you talk like that. Are you sure you want to go back?" She seemed quite moved by his desire to return to his own family.

"Yeah, I think so, Sandy. I really think so. I hope you don't mind." Billy was afraid that her next words might make him want to reconsider his decision.

"I'm really proud of you, Snick," she replied softly. "I hope you can make everything work out all right." Then she walked over to the teenager and hugged him. The embrace was **vastly** different from the one they had shared in Waikiki. This time, the affection was more sincere and **empathetic** than self-seeking and **passionate**. She really cared for him.

"Twinks, I'll never forget you," Billy whispered in her ear as they clung to one another.

"Thanks, Billy. But don't try too hard to remember me. Just remember that there are people in the world who really do love you." She then kissed him affectionately on the side of his cheek, releasing her hold on him and returning to her packing.

"Here's a carry-bag for you, Billy," Sandy continued, noticing that the young traveler had nothing to put his clothes into. "I hope you can fit everything in it, but take your time. Tom's in his room, probably reading another of *Karl Marx's* **manifestos**. He'll be there for hours."

The conversation between the two was concluded for a while, each **preoccupied** with their future directions, neither able to come up with the right words to add to further the discussion. All that needed to be said was said; the rest was felt. They were still friends, they would always be friends. But Billy now felt the **exhilaration** of the new path that awaited him.

CHAPTER XXVI
The Confession

By noon, Sandy was fully packed and ready to leave. Billy's clothes had fit comfortably into his tote bag, and he spent the rest of the morning watching Sandy **scamper** back and forth, placing everything as precisely as possible into the three suitcases she had brought out.

"What are you planning on doing?" Billy asked, breaking the silence as Sandy **secured** the luggage.

"Well, Snick, I've managed to live my entire life searching for independence, and I've found it every so often. But whenever I find myself losing it I tend to move on to keep that independence. It's not something that everyone wants, and I don't think I envy people who need to be so free. There's probably a good side to family living, but I never really had any and so I've never missed it. I just keep away from that kind of lifestyle. I'm not afraid of it; I just don't like what I've seen of it."

"But haven't you ever been in someone's house where the family treats you like one of them?" Billy asked, hopeful to shed some light on the reason for Sandy's **willful nomadic** existence.

"No, can't say that I have. I guess I just didn't grow up in middle-America. I was always escaping the scene, not joining it. My brother and I were close, but he died in *Nam*. Maybe that snapped me a little. I don't even want to think about it. I've blocked it out so well, it hurts to bring it back now. Yeah, maybe it all **stemmed** from James' death. I don't know, Snick. He was only nineteen when he was killed. I was only fifteen." Sandy stopped working for the moment and continued. "I can remember the day it happened. He'd been drafted by Johnson's men and was in *Nam* before we could even protest. He wanted to go to college but he registered late and got stuck instantly with a **1-A**. He was gone the next month. Two months later, he came back in a box. The day before it happened, I remember getting our community college to grant a special late-admission for James, and I went home to tell my folks. They were never on the ball, always in their own spaced-out world. Maybe it was drugs or overwork, I don't know, but they always had an excuse for everything. They never tried to help us. They claimed they were giving us the freedom we needed. Sure, they gave us the rope to hang ourselves with, and that's what happened to James, though someone else did it for him. Anyway, when I got the paperwork all ready, we got that letter from the President. Registered and impersonal, and we all knew what it said. 'We regret to inform you...' That's all I needed to read. Mom cried, but it was almost **hypocritical**. She'd never helped before, so why did she have the right to cry for my brother? He was killed on the day before he was accepted into the college. We had received the acceptance letter and I had just sent him the papers to sign. But he obviously never received it. I hope someone else got the papers instead and maybe got out of that **God-forsaken** place."

"So what happened to you after all that?" Billy asked, seated on the sofa and listening **intently**.

"I guess I freaked out. I packed up a few things and ran away. I couldn't stand it there anymore.

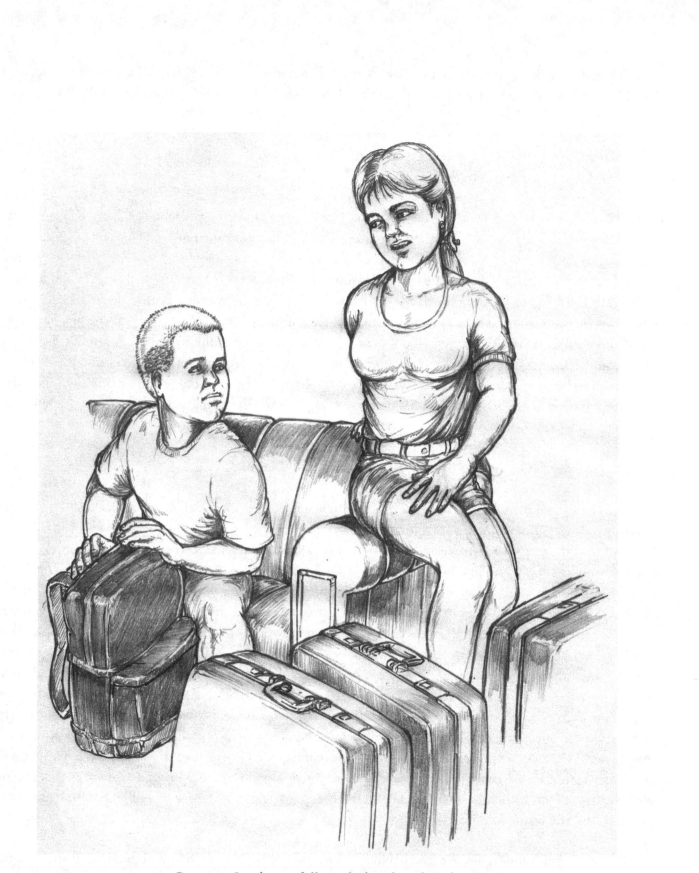

By noon, Sandy was fully packed and ready to leave.

Everything in my life died when James died. I needed to start over." Sandy paused a moment, reflecting. "And I guess I'm still running away from that day. I don't know, Billy. I really don't know. Will I ever find peace? Do you think I will?"

"I sure hope so, Twinks. You're such a beautiful person. You rescued me, that's for sure. If James were watching, I know he'd be proud of you."

The words hit close to Sandy's heart, and she hung her head and began to sob. "Billy, I love you for everything you've been for me. How can I even begin to explain how much of James I see in you? And you just seem to be more sensitive with every word. You just don't know how precious you are to me. How can I thank you, Billy? God, give me the words to tell you how I feel." She then walked over and knelt at Billy's side, stroking and kissing his hand. "Billy, you've become the younger brother I never had. You've let me offer you everything I can, just like James offered me everything he had. He was the best brother a girl could ever want, and yet he never ever knew what the world was going to give back to him. For every kind word he had for me, the world spit on him in return. And to help me, he sacrificed himself. He didn't go to college because of me, Billy. He wanted to stay home and watch out for me while my folks were traveling. He got killed because of me, and now you've given me the chance to give back just a small piece of myself."

"You saved my life, Sandy. I'll never forget what you did for me."

"And you saved my life, too, Billy. You've given me a new life, a new chance to start over, but this time without feeling guilty about myself. You did it because you never asked me 'Why?' Maybe that's what we need to do: Accept each other and not try to ask 'Why?' Those scriptures are full of deceit. And the entire 'cause' is simply one big **façade**. Tom and his professional **platitudes**, all full of **cryptic** confusion and meaningless talk. Do you know the reason he wanted us to get other people to ask 'Why?' Isn't it obvious? If others asked 'Why?' then he wouldn't have to try to find the answer himself. By having others ask 'Why?' he could hide behind the fact that he had no answer. Tom wanted us to ask other people what he didn't even know himself. Do you really think he could answer that question himself? Try asking him if you see him. He's great at messing up other people's minds, because it's a lot easier than trying to straighten out his own. It's much easier to criticize others than to better yourself. But Billy, you showed me just how important it is to take responsibility for yourself, to learn to value your own judgments and not worry about trying to affect others. You changed my attitude because you know what you want. Somehow, your innocence has been more powerful than all our years of **misguided** world-revolutionizing. Whatever you've got, it's worth a lot. Maybe it's innocence, maybe you're just possessed with god-sent magic, or maybe you're just in touch with your own feelings. But whatever, you got me to see myself, and you've made me proud to feel the way I do now."

The long confession of discovery left Billy at a loss for words. No one had flattered him at such length and in such logical fashion. His parents might have felt that way about him, but they never expressed it anywhere near as openly as this.

"Thanks, Twinks. Thanks for everything. I'll never forget you, either. You did save my life, and maybe you've helped me to know what I need to do if I can go back. I need to say more and not just think about it. I need to express my feelings and not just dream about them. I guess we each need to start over. We did save each other, didn't we, after all!" Billy added joyfully. "That makes us 'even'!"

"No, Snick, that makes us 'friends.' Friends don't have to keep track of who's even and who's not. And I think we'll be friends forever if you'll let me know where I can contact you –"

Billy didn't hesitate. "1111 Oceanside Street. Billy Steele, with an 'e' at the end. The zip's 96816 and the phone number's 951-1644." He then hesitated for a moment. "But don't get in touch with me too soon. I really don't know where I'm headed right now. There's still a lot I'm not sure about."

"Well, Snick, what counts is that you're thinking about your future, and so am I. And even if we take it slowly, one day at a time, we'll eventually get there. I sure hope you get back to where you belong; but whatever you do, I pray that you'll be happy. I'll hope and wish and pray for you every day and every night, Snick. Just like I used to do for James."

Sandy then picked up the suitcases, placing Billy's address and phone number safely in her back pants-pocket. "So I guess this is 'goodbye,' my little brother. Take care of yourself, please."

"I will, Twinks, I sure will. For you."

"No, do it for you, not for me," she replied tenderly. "Remember that you've got to take care of 'Number One' first, and that's you. Don't ever let anyone else tell you how to lead your life. Follow your own dream and you'll always be happy."

"I will, Twinks. And I know you will, too. For me and for you."

The two exchanged their final smiles, each one **surveying** the other from head to foot, sad to see the journey nearing its end. The road now would need to be traveled individually. Billy raised his hand and waved goodbye as Sandy opened the front door and exited into the freshness of the afternoon.

As the door closed, Tom poked his head out from behind his bedroom door. "Did Sandy just go out?" he asked.

"Yes she did, Tom," Billy replied quietly.

"Do you know when she's coming back? I'm getting hungry."

Billy chuckled somewhat sadly to himself, realizing how accurately Sandy had described Tom's character. "I think she'll be gone awhile. But don't worry, I'm sure she'll be back home soon enough."

Tom could never have guessed what Billy was **alluding** to, instead remarking "Good, then we can start planning our next moves."

Sandy had already planned hers.

CHAPTER XXVII
Starting Over

Billy waited awhile before leaving. He needed to plan his next steps, aware that he was now headed back out on the streets again, hiding from the police and from anyone else who might recognize him. The direction still wasn't clear. It was nearly three o'clock, the Palmview students having gotten out from school thirty minutes earlier. He feared seeing anyone he knew. If he tried to return home, was seen by someone who recognized him and was **subsequently** picked up by the police, his entire experience would be **construed** as a **sensationalized fiasco**. He would be returned like a **fugitive**, and everything he had gained on his own would be blanketed by **degradation**. If he were to go back home, he would want to do so by himself, willingly and without **fanfare** or humiliation. Sandy's words revolved about him like a halo and guiding light: "...value your own judgments and don't worry about trying to affect others." It made more sense than Butch's **gratuitous** advice about escaping to the streets.

Billy picked up the telephone receiver and dialed Stewart's number. Maybe the **weary wayfarer** could **glean** some guidance from a discussion with his best friend.

Stewart answered the phone quietly.

"Hi Stew, it's Billy."

"I knew you'd call again," Stewart shouted **gleefully**. "I knew it. Sooner or later. Fantastic! How's it been with you, Snick?" Stewart was almost beside himself with happiness. The words rebounded off Billy and sent a momentary thrill of **ebullient optimism** throughout his body.

"I'm all right, Stew. You sound good, too."

"Gee, Snick, I hoped you'd call sooner than later. And I didn't tell anyone about you. You can count on that. Nobody else knows you're still around." Stewart paused to catch his thoughts and his breath. "So where are you headed for now? Still in the same place?"

"How come so many questions, Stew?" Billy asked with a lighthearted laugh.

"Oh, I don't know. Maybe because I'm such a nosy guy. And you know, school's over in six weeks. Then it's summertime. Surf, skateboards and girls. It'll be a real gas this year."

Stewart was obviously trying to **entice** Billy to return, but the words didn't offer the way back. Billy was more bold.

"Okay, so what do I do, Stew? Tell me, okay?"

Stewart was silent for a moment. "Gee, I didn't think you'd ask me that. Wow, you're really tired of what you've been doing?"

"Not really that. But I think I learned what I needed to, so now I want to see if there's a way back."

Stewart echoed confidently, "There's always a way back if you want to get back. Nobody can stop you from doing what you want."

The words **resonated** with familiarity, the image of the blonde-haired youthful girl seeking her own identity flashing through Billy's mind. Sandy was right. And so was Stewart. "Well, then, Stewart, I guess I need to figure out the way, huh?"

But Stewart couldn't help beyond merely suggesting the solution. "It's your choice, my friend. You gotta figure out how to do it. But I'm sure glad you want to come back. I can't believe how good it feels."

"Thanks for saying that, Stew. You don't know how good that really sounds."

"Well, now that we both feel so good, what are you gonna do about it?"

"I guess we'll both just have to wait and see. I can't say for sure. Maybe there's a way, maybe there isn't. I really don't know right now. But don't tell anyone I called, okay?"

Stewart's happiness **drooped**. "So you don't know for sure what you'll do?"

"No, I really don't. It's not that easy. Sometimes the key fits but the lock is jammed. I think I've gotta take some time to figure out if I can un-jam the lock. But you're right – I've got the key. Now I just gotta figure out what to do with it."

Billy thought to himself for a moment. Nothing had **altered** his desire to return home, but neither was it any clearer how to do so. Billy did discover, nonetheless, that his best friend wanted him to return, but finding the right path home was still **problematical**. "Stew, I'll contact you again in a day or so, okay? Maybe then I'll know what to do. I may just stick around here a little while longer. But keep smiling. You know I won't let you down. That's what friends are for."

As he hung up the receiver, Billy knew he had to set out on his own and head wherever the direction pointed. He couldn't stay with Tom alone.

Pitching his large **satchel** over his back, the **peregrine** pilgrim took his chances and headed out to Waikiki. He realized he urgently needed to make a **pivotal** decision, one which would doubtless prove both **momentous** and frighteningly **irrevocable**. His future was at stake, but at this **juncture** there could be no turning back, for he had nowhere else to go.

Billy Steele knew he would have time to think matters over on the bus and at the *Waikiki Video Factory*, but he also was **starkly** aware that his options were all but gone.

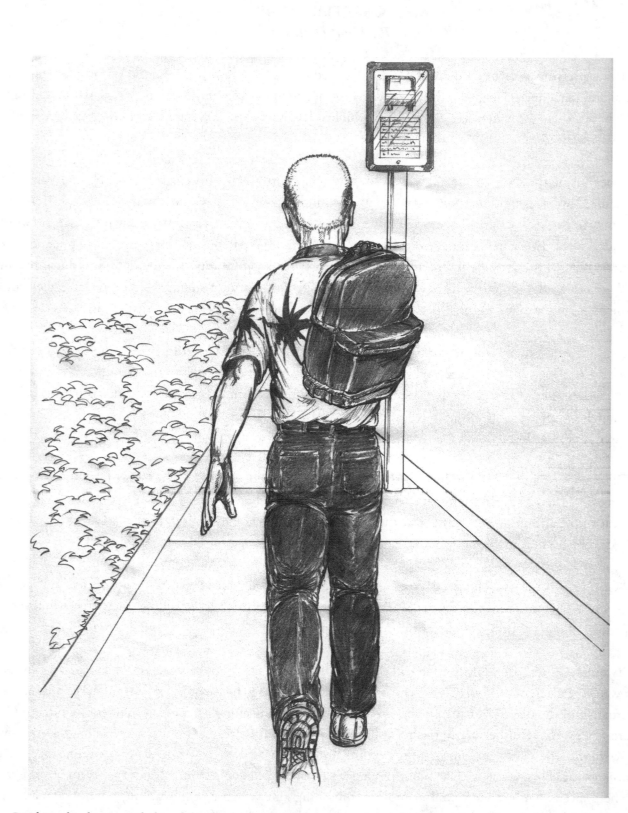

Pitching his large satchel over his back, the peregrine pilgrim took his chances and headed out to Waikiki.

CHAPTER XXVIII
The Final Destination

The walk from the bus to the video parlor seemed to take forever for the young traveler, an especially critical and **perilous trek** because Billy feared that someone might recognize who he was. Fortunately, in his flashy blue pants and matching shirt he hardly looked like a teenage runaway; he had no problem arriving at his destination.

Once inside the dark arcade, Billy was safe and able to **immerse** himself in one of the many different fictionalized worlds. He ventured into a new one, finding himself in a maze trying to escape from tiny gremlins. In this new **labyrinthine** video game, he found himself taking turns not knowing where he would be headed next. Every new tunnel led to more obstacles, more **rapacious** gremlins and more uncertainties. "C'mon, Billy, you can make it," he **reassured** himself. "Just keep heading for the light and don't give up. You'll get out all right." While he played, he seemed to be formulating and reinforcing his strategy not only for the game but also for his own personal **predicament**. The advice fit for both situations.

As the battle progressed, he continued fighting **dauntlessly** and **doggedly** against the invisible enemy – the future. One tunnel passageway would close, forcing him to dash back to find another, always staying just a few steps ahead of the tiny monsters who were equally determined to devour him. As they got closer, the tunnels finally began to straighten and point the way out. The **proverbial** 'light at the end of the tunnel' appeared, and his **alter ego** ran for the shelter of clear skies. The alien forces couldn't hurt him anymore.

Billy stopped and turned to look outside at the late-afternoon sunlight which cast long shadows upon the streets. "There's still enough time," he murmured to himself. He knew he had to decide quickly what to do, for now and forever. The light at the end of the tunnel was fading fast, but whatever the decision it needed to be his and his alone.

"Gotta catch the bus," he cried aloud. Grabbing his bag, Billy raced out of the arcade and jumped on the bus just as it was about to depart Waikiki. There was no time to lose, and he knew that whatever his next move, there was only one direction for him to pursue.

Twenty minutes later, Billy stepped off the Kaimuki bus and stared at the streets he had missed for the past four weeks, the neighborhood in which he had grown up. Years ago he treasured every tree, every house, every square inch of the place. But then he began to find it boring, meaningless and a reminder of a directionless future. Now, those earlier memories returned as he gazed teary-eyed in the direction where his very own house stood. The streets no longer appeared directionless. Instead, they acquired added significance. They **commemorated** his very existence, pointing the way to where he lived, belonged and was proud of. The trees each held special significance, one after another containing some artwork, some carving that he had made over the course of his young life. He had etched his mark on them and would be **immortalized** for being himself, not some **cog** in the larger machinery called a 'cause.' This was his neighborhood, and he didn't want to lose the

Twenty minutes later, Billy stepped off the Kaimuki bus...

intimate memories he had **cherished** as a child. Sandy never enjoyed the benefit of a secure childhood, and as a result she had to run around acting young to overcome this **deficiency**. But a person can never relive one's youth, not without **tangible mementos** of how it was. And here, in front of Billy, all the memories of his **halcyon** youth and all his future memories would await him for as long as he should choose to acknowledge them.

As he passed by each tree and every portion of sidewalk decorated with graffiti, he paused to read the writing. "Billy was here," the first writing he had ever done in cement. He was only seven years old then, but every **vivid** detail of that memorable occasion came back to life as he stared down at the primitive etching. He'd come a long way since then, but the words hadn't really changed. He still wanted to be "Billy," not some revolutionary activist or some teenage rebel. The only cause he wanted to pursue was his own cause: being himself. He didn't need to find another identity. He'd discovered the true one beneath the **restive recalcitrance** that **decried** a life of **mediocrity** and boredom. In **sooth**, the only **mediocrity** came from his own unwillingness to do more, and he now realized that any limitations in his life were **self-effected**. He couldn't blame his parents for his own **shortcomings**. The streets had shown him one lesson, one which Tom and Sandy echoed so accurately: his life was his life, no one else's. And in taking the responsibility, he also had to accept the **concomitant** consequences, whether good or bad, and make the most out of what he had. Following his strategy in the new video game he had just played, Billy knew he needed to reach out for the light – to **resolve** his problems by **striving** for the answers.

"I think I'm gonna make it," he said to himself with **certitude** as he continued the **trek** toward home. If anyone recognized him, he was determined to just walk on by and ignore the temporary interruption. He had one goal in mind, one light to reach, even though he had no idea what would be on the other side of the tunnel.

As Oceanside Street neared, Billy's heart pumped faster and faster. He could see the corner house with its green-and-white border and the beautifully-trimmed garden, looking as though it were cared for by a family of gardeners rather than a teacher and a banker and their two teenage sons.

Once on the street, he could see his own house, 1111 printed boldly on the silver mailbox. The brown trim matched tastefully with the off-white color of the house itself, surrounded artistically by hedges sporting white and red jasmine flowers.

But there seemed a dullness about the house as Billy approached and looked beyond the stairs to the front porch. The house looked **dingier** and less well-cared-for than usual, as though it had been neglected for a few weeks. Even the front lawn he **traversed** showed signs of yellowing, a **telltale** indication that these were indeed not the best of times for its caretakers.

Billy stood silently in front of his house, under the fading five-o'clock Hawaiian sunshine, dressed in his blue shirt and pants, the same he had worn when he had **surreptitiously emblazoned** his message in Waikiki just a few days earlier. But this time he had no pens along and wasn't

Billy stood silently in front of his house...

seeking **evanescent adulation**. His life had become much too **dear**, and now he wished only to be appreciated for who he really was, not who he pretended to be. This house was real, not a **fleeting illusion** in the middle of a **plastic** city. This was home. His home. And the only thought that ran through his mind was what he would say when his mom answered the door, if indeed she wasn't working.

How would he reintroduce himself after all the weeks? Perhaps he could explain why he left, or maybe just claim that he was kidnapped. Thoughts raced through his mind as he walked slowly up the steps and approached the front door.

There was so much he could say, anything from the truth to a collection of assorted half-truths to a **fabrication** of **unmitigated** lies. Everything seemed possible, and yet he couldn't say them all.

The doorbell rang, and he knew the next few moments would be the most **fateful** and **consequential** in all his young life. How would his mother react? Would she hit him? Would she throw him out of the house? Or worse yet, would she ignore him? And what if she didn't answer the door? What would he do then? Return to the streets? Or hide until they arrived? Could he even bear to wait that long?

The front door began to open, and Billy knew that he would soon find his answers, no matter what they were. All his thoughts became jumbled together, the truth and the lies, and he could feel his throat lump up inside of him. Would he even be able to **utter** a syllable? Or would he be **muted** in shock? He prayed for the right words, anything to help return him back to his home.

The door opened, and Billy stared straight into the eyes of his mother. The two looked at each other, stunned. No words were spoken. Billy began to shake. Tears began to fall. His whole body started to **gyrate**, a sense of helpless unconsciousness falling over him.

"I've come home, mom," he said calmly and then collapsed into the waiting arms of his mother.

END

THEME SONG
From The Other Side
Lyrics by Raymond Karelitz

Give me a chance to see life from the other side;
Let me look at my life from the other side.
Then I can see where my future truly lies;
Let me see life from the other side.

I've grown to doubt and question what I'm living for;
I need a new horizon to call my very own.
But it's from the other side this dream I must explore
To find a newer meaning than that I've ever known.

Give me a chance to see life from the other side;
Let me look at my life from the other side.
Then I can see where my future truly lies;
Let me see life from the other side.

And if I venture to a new world beyond
And find the dreams I never had before,
I may discover words to a never-written song;
The song I'll sing of freedom at another's door.

Give me a chance to see life from the other side;
Let me look at my life from the other side.
Then I can see where my future truly lies;
Let me see life from the other side.

Don't hold me back from whatever comes my way;
Just let me travel on my road free and proud.
I need to find my future, no matter where it's paved;
My destiny beckons from beyond the crowd.

Give me a chance to see life from the other side;
Let me look at life from the other side.
Then I will know where my future truly lies,
Once I've seen life from the other side.

Even Odds

Glossary

The following words (deemed by the editor to be of challenging difficulty and of particular value in college writing and in entrance exams such as the S.A.T.) appear in this novel. Each word is then defined briefly in its context.

You are encouraged to purchase a marking-pen which accentuates text, highlight unfamiliar key words as they appear, and complete the highlighting process by accentuating the glossary-definition of the word.

This process of word-building through reading and highlighting will not only help you add to your vocabulary, but it will also help introduce you to the highly effective method of highlighting for future readings as well!

1-A (128) eligible to be immediately drafted

abandon (2, 109) impulsive enthusiasm / wildness and unconstraint

Abbott (7) Abbott and Costello were a comedy team (pun intended on the name switch)

abiding (17) tolerating

abounds (109) is plentiful

abridgment (64) restriction

absconding (43) fleeing

accede (72, 106) consent

accentuated (34) gave emphasis to / marked with emphasis

accord (31) agreement ("of his own accord" / voluntarily)

acquiescence (78) consent

acrimonious (105, 119) hostile and spiteful

acute (55) painful

adamantly (15) insistently

addled (113) confused

adeptness (3) skill

admonished (83) cautioned / warned

ado (51) bustling activity / commotion

adolescent (5, 100) teenage

Adonis (116) [Greek Mythology] a handsome youth

adorned (30, 62) decorated

adulation (140) lavish praise

adventitiously (56) accidentally / unexpectedly

adventuresome (43) risk taking

adversarial (122) bitterly opposing

adversaries (56) enemies / opponents

advisement (103) advice

aegis (106) sponsorship

aesthetically (91, 103) artistically

affirmatively (78) in a positive manner

affront (7) insult

aggression (121) hostility

air (9, 113) manner

akin (43) related / similar

à la (44) in the manner of

alacrity (39) cheerful eagerness

albeit (105) even though

alibi (29) excuse (often made up)

alienate (9) make angry / hostile

aligned (87) ordered in a straight line

alighted (105) descended

allayed (70) soothed

allies (70) partners

allotted (87) appropriate

alluding (132) indirectly referring

alluring (40) attractive and appealing

ally (6) friend and associate

aloof (116) removed and uninvolved

alter (3, 98, 136) change

alter ego (136) a second or other self (as controlled by an inner, subconscious voice)

altercation (119) angry dispute

altruistic (21) charitable / benevolent

amassed (72) accumulated

ambiguous (76) vague

ambled (18) walked slowly and leisurely

ambrosial (62) delicious

ameliorate (58) improve

amigo (25) [Spanish] friend

ample (18, 22) adequate / sufficient

anachronistic (58) chronologically out of place

analogy (103) comparison

animated (20) aroused

animation (13) liveliness

animus (122) hatred

annals (16) historical records

annihilation (71) complete destruction and ruin

antagonism (113) hostility

antagonist (52) rival

antagonistic (119) hostile

antagonize (7, 49) arouse the hostility of

anti-apartheid (69) opposed to the official policy of racial segregation

anticipatory (87) anticipating

antiquated (64) old

anxiety (70, 101, 115) uneasiness

apocalypse (85) revelation

apocryphal (78) of dubious authenticity

apoplectic (56) relating to Apoplexy - a sudden loss of bodily function due to a stroke

apostle (71) disciple

apotheosis (49) ideal

appeased (31) satisfied

appellation (119) name / title

appendage (98) limb

applicable (113) relevant

appraisal (6, 126) evaluation

apprenticeship (69) training

apprised (83) informed

approbation (21) approval

appropriating (21) taking

apropos (64) appropriate

apt (7, 21, 69, 125) suitable / appropriate

arbiters (78) judges

ardor (25, 94) passion

arduous (55) difficult

aristocracy (22) ruling class

aromatically (60) fragrantly

array (30, 39) arrangement

arrayed (85, 96) organized

arrogance (116) unwarranted show of pride and superiority

artful (76) skillful

artful dodger (103) clever young character in Charles Dickens' novel

articulate (113) express

artifice (21) clever scheme

artillery (72) collection of guns and other weapons

artlessness (21) naiveté

ascending (89) climbing

ascertained (58) determined

aspersions (105) hurtful statements

aspiration (69, 89) ambition / goal

aspiring (18) seeking ambitiously

assault (119) attack

assayed (64) analyzed the worth of

assertively (74) positively and insistently / forcefully

assess (34, 55) evaluate

assessment (6, 125) evaluation

assimilating (74) absorbing

assuaged (67) soothed

astounded (67) amazed and confused

astringent (7) austere / stern

asylums (49) shelters

attaining (63) accomplishing

attenuated (122) weakened / reduced

attire (89, 96, 105) clothes

attribute (103) quality / characteristic

attributes (14) inherent qualities

atypical (2) abnormal

audacious (107) extremely bold and daring

auguring (18) forecasting

aura (22) distinctive quality / distinctive atmosphere

auspicious (18, 107) favorable

austere (29) lacking comforts

autonomy (2, 98) self-rule

auxiliary (21) assisting / supplementary

aversion (17, 64) strong dislike

avert (51) avoid

avid (105) eager

awry (16) wrong

azure (61) clear blue

baleful (96) evil

balked (55) hesitated

bamboozled (100) deceived

barbs (17) pointed, sarcastic remarks

barrage (76) sudden, large quantity

barter (44) the exchange of goods

beacon (61) guiding light

bearing (48, 87) sense of direction

beck (21) beckoning

beckon (1, 8, 39, 96) summon / attract

befall (17, 107) happen to

befit (15, 94, 105) be suitable for

befriend (91) make friends with

befuddled (15) confused

beguiling (95) charming

behemoth (52) giant

belabor (103) overdo

belied (7, 110, 122) misrepresented / showed differently than

belligerence (7) hostile / warlike

bellow (9, 24, 46) roar in a deep, loud tone

bemused (15) stunned / bewildered

benefactor (56) kindly helper

beneficent (18) kindly

benevolent (58, 106) charitable

benign (56) kind and friendly

bereft (99) deprived

beseeched (51) begged

bespoke (58) reflected

bestowing (65) granting

bevy (18) flock / group

bewildered (79, 103) puzzled and confused

bland (1) unexciting

blatant (29, 75, 83) clearly obvious

bliss (61, 67) joy

blissful (43) joyful

blithely (18) merrily

blushingly (75) red-faced through embarrassment

Bogey (33) see ***Humphrey Bogart***

bolster (105, 122) support

bolted (27, 92) dashed / fled

bondage (2) slavery

booty (43) prize / seized goods

bounding (64) leaping

boundless (11, 18) unlimited

bravado (88, 113) show of bravery / showy and daring display of courage

brawny (34) muscular

breach (122) break / gap

brevity (58) briefness

brink (115) edge

brisk (63) refreshing

brooked (64) tolerated

brusquely (52) rudely sudden and forceful

buffoon (7) clown

buoyant (116) lively

burgeoning (46) flourishing

burly (52) heavy and strong

bustling (2) busy and active / moving quickly and busily

cache (49) items hidden / stored

cacophonous (27) inharmonious / discordant

cadence (61) rhythmic flow

cajole (21) coax

calculated (125) carefully thought out

callow (21, 106) immature / inexperienced

camaraderie (25) close friendship

caper (102) wild escapade

capitalism (67, 107) economic system based on capitalistic ideals

capitalistic (64, 67) relating to a financially-motivated society

capitulate (31) surrender

capitulatory (87) giving in

captivate (41) charm

captivating (1, 67) fascinating

caress (61) gently stroke

cataclysmic (43, 80) violent and earth-shaking

catalyst (6) stimulus

cautionary (25, 69) serving to warn

cavalierly (21) arrogantly

caveat (89) warning

cavorting (95) playful merrymaking

celerity (44) swiftness

certitude (138) certainty

chagrin (94) embarrassment and humility

championed (107) fought for

chaos (69) turmoil

chaotic (60) confused / disorderly

Charleston (64) early 20th century dance

check (13) restrain

cherished (2, 126, 138) held dear

chimerically (11, 126) wildly fanciful

circadian (43) daily

circumscribed (6, 31) limited

circumscription (16, 17) restriction

circumspect (109) cautious and alert

clad (21, 96, 105) clothed

clamor (55) noise

clandestine (83) secretive

clarion (67) clear

clemency (11) mercy

cloak-and-dagger (83) undercover / spying

coax (14) persuade

coexistence (106) state of living together

cog (136) minor part

cogitated (40, 56) pondered

cognizant (98) aware

collaborated (69, 102) worked together

collaborative (105) working together

collusive (74) collaborative

comestibles (62) food

commemorate (60, 136) honor the memory of / serve as a memory

commenced (43) began

commingled (109) mixed together

communal (106) shared in a community

commune (106) community of group living

communion (60) get together

compassion (40, 114, 115) a feeling of sympathy and understanding for another

compassionate (58, 62) kindhearted

compatriots (69, 74) colleagues or fellow countrymen / companions

compelled (3, 67, 100, 126) drive / urge on

complexities (79) complications

components (127) ingredients

comported (116) conducted

comrade (5, 37) friend

comradeship (69) friendship

conceded (9) acknowledged

concession (106) acknowledgement

conciliatory (119) pacifying

concomitant (138) accompanying

concrete (100) tangible

concurred (75) agreed

condescending (11) acting as if superior and lowering oneself to address another

confabulation (78) informal discussion

confide (89) reveal one's personal secrets trustfully

conform (17, 126) obey / act in accordance

conformity (106) submission / obeying the rules

confreres (100) cohorts / associates

confront (3, 7) challenge face to face (in battle)

confronted (98) faced

conjectured (76) speculated

conjure (43) devise / imagine

conscientious (60) careful / painstaking

consequential (140) significant in its consequences

conservatively (103) traditional in style

console (98) comfort / lessen the grief and sadness of

consorting (46) socializing

conspicuously (44) easily seen / noticed

consternation (92) sudden fear

constrictive (31) limiting

constructive (60) productive

construed (7, 133) interpreted

consummated (43) climaxed

contemplate (6, 24, 42, 51) consider deeply and seriously

contemporary (3) modern / current-day

contended (64) argued in opposition

contour (34, 84) curving line

convention (83, 106) established custom

conversing (94) talking informally

conviction (11, 122) strong belief

convulsion (92) spasm

convulsive (58) involving convulsions

coquettish (95) flirtatious

cordial (61) friendly

cordoned (44) blockaded / obstructed

cornucopia (62) diverse abundance

corruption (64, 69, 72) dishonest / immoral

cosmetically (103) through the use of beauty aids, especially for the skin

countenance (7, 112) outward (facial) appearance

counteracting (79) offsetting

counterculture (76, 106) against the social mainstream

countermand (41) revoke and replace a previous order

covert (109) secret and hidden

coveted (3) desired greedily

coyly (62, 110) pretending to be shy and bashful

crafted (6, 87) skillfully made

cranium (33) skull

crave (2) desire

credulous (100) gullible

crescendo (121) gradual climax

crisis (123) critical period of time

crowning (67, 87) climactic

crusade (107) idealistic mission

cryptic (76, 85, 115, 130) puzzling and unclear

cue (17) signal

culinary (60) relating to cooking

culminate (105) climax

curator (61) caretaker

curb (40) control

curfew (21, 27, 49) regulation restricting a specified group (i.e. minors) from frequenting the streets after a certain hour

curious (105) unusual / odd

curtly (112) in a rude and brief manner

dabble (21) involve casually and occasionally

daredevil (109) recklessly bold / adventurous

dauntlessly (136) courageously

deafening (5) extremely loud

dear (140) precious

dearth (21) lack / scarcity

debilitate (55, 99) weaken

decamp (6, 106) flee / leave suddenly

deceptive (64) intentionally misleading

declamatory (64) loudly critical

decried (138) denounced

defiant (113) boldly challenging

deficiency (138) something inadequate

defunct (107) dead / no longer functioning

defuse (52) make harmless / powerless

defying (121) challenging

degenerate (122) worsen

degradation (133) shame and humiliation

delegated (71) assigned

deliberate (11) careful

deliberately (121) slowly and carefully

deliberation (31, 109) careful and unhurried thinking

deliverance (40, 70) rescue from danger

delusory (3) deceptive / misleading

demeaning (9) degrading

demeanor (18, 87, 109) outward manner / behavior

denoted (21) meant

densely (96) thickly

depleted (42) used up

deprivation (25) state of being deprived

derelict (49) negligent

deride (105) ridicule

derision (17) ridicule

desolate (31) gloomy and uninhabited

desolately (61) uninhabitedly

desolation (123) loneliness

destiny (5, 13, 16, 17, 31, 63, 98) fate

desultory (13) aimless

detached (21, 112) distant

detested (106) hated

deviate (87) stray

devotee (81) ardent follower

dexterity (91) manual skillfulness

diatribe (64, 72) bitter denunciation

dictating (78) ordering

dictatorial (100) absolute

didactically (72) giving instruction

differentiate (96) distinguish

diffuse (64) wordy

digest (62) mentally absorb

dignified (98, 105) honorable

digression (13) straying from the main topic

digressive (6, 64) rambling

dilatory (109) delaying

dilemma (100) difficult situation, problem or choice

diligently (64) in a hard working manner

diminutive (11) tiny

din (44) confused noise

dingier (138) dirtier / shabbier

directives (17) orders

disabuse (126) enlighten

disaffection (60) discontent

discarded (71) thrown away

discerned (96) distinguished / identified

disciple (105) follower

discomposure (62) uneasiness

discordant (122) clashing

discourse (58, 99, 122) communication / conversation

discreetly (105) carefully / thoughtfully prudent

discretion (76) individual choice

disdained (62) scorned

disengaged (112) withdrawn

dismal (40) gloomy

disparaging (105) insulting

dispatch (85) send out

dispersed (2) spread out

disportment (44) behavior

disposal (52, 116) command / control

disposition (56, 101) spirit or nature / mood

disputatious (119) argumentative

disquietude (99) state of uneasiness / agitation

dissent (64, 107) disagree

dissipating (60) becoming less concentrated

dissuade (5) persuade against

distinct (3, 96) clearly separate

distinguish (49, 96, 105) separate

distort (121) alter the meaning of

distracted (6) sidetracked

diurnal (39) daily

diversion (100) pastime / recreation

divert (20) amuse / entertain

divine (43, 60) as though from a god-like power

divisive (126) causing friction

divorced (24, 110) separated

divulge (94) reveal (as a secret)

doctrinaire (119) dogmatic

doctrine (64) belief

documenting (72) authenticating

doffed (95) took off

doggedly (136) stubbornly

dogmas (119) set of beliefs

dogmatic (64) set in one's beliefs

domain (62) territory

domestic (2, 109) relating to the home

don (40, 62) put on

Don Juan (20) [literature] infamous lover

dormantly (69) in an inactive state

double entendre (21) a word / expression with two meanings.

doughty (3) fearless and determined

dour (112) gloomy / sullen

drab (56, 105) dull and dreary

dreaded (11, 40, 110) feared

drooped (134) weakened

dudgeon (122) anger

dulcet (21) sweet-sounding

dumbfounded (65, 110) speechless with amazement

dwelt (17, 87) directed one's attention

dynamic (43, 72) forceful and energetic

earnest (5, 64, 101, 113) seriousness and with sincere feeling

ebullient (133) enthusiastic

ecstatic (114) extremely joyful

effect (126) produce

effectuate (21) make happen / accomplish

effervescent (87) excited

efficient (21) effective

effulgence (43) radiance / brilliance

ego (13, 67) self-pride

elaborate (30) fancy

elaborate (113, 116) explain in greater detail

elapsed (91) passed

eleemosynary (25) charitable

eliciting (18) bringing forth

elite (89) socially superior

elude (49) avoid / escape

Elysian (17) heavenly

emanating (100) coming forth

emancipation (22) freedom / liberation

embark (16) begin / start

embedded (25) fixed firmly

embellished (105) enhanced / decorated

embellishment (91) decoration

emblazoned (44, 138) decorated in brilliant colors

embody (56) incorporate

embraced (64) accepted

embroidering (91) adorning

embryonic (20, 43) undeveloped

emergence (106) appearance

emissary (89) delegate / messenger

empathetic (127) sharing feelings

empathy (115) compassion

emphatically (46) forcefully

employing (14, 21) utilizing

empyreal (43) heavenly

encapsulate (76, 106) condense by summarizing

encore (1) additional song to satisfy a demand

encounter (15, 17, 51, 94) meet

encroach (62, 96) intrude / trespass

endeavor (13, 33, 55, 69, 76) serious determined effort / undertaking

endorsed (109) supported

enervating (54) causing weakness and physical helplessness

enfeebled (56) weakened

engage (22, 27) enter into a challenge

engage (64, 89) involve

engage (20) occupy the attention of

engendered (17, 40) produced / gave life to

engineered (110) planned and organized

engrossed (49, 94) deeply absorbed and interested

enhanced (103) intensified

enigmatic (107) mysterious and secretive

enmity (17) hatred

ennui (17) boredom

enterprise (74, 83) undertaking

enthrallment (81) charming spell

entice (3, 22, 40, 133) lure / attract

entranced (22, 96) hypnotically fascinating

entreated (15) begged

entrée (88) entrance / admittance

envision (17, 114) imagine

epic (87) majestic

epigrammatic (103) witty

epigrams (76) witty sayings

epileptic (43) displayed by fits / seizures

epithets (105) obscenities

epitomizing (69) representing ideally

equable (44) even-tempered / calm

equilibrium (43) balance

errant (84) wandering

escalated (121) increased in intensity

eschewed (121) avoided

espied (44, 56, 100) caught sight of / noticed

espionage (64) spying

espoused (22) advocated

essayed (55) attempted

Establishment (69, 72) powerful group in control of society

esteem (65, 84) admiration / respect

estranged (106) separated / feeling no close attraction to

estrangement (114) separation

ethereal (33) heavenly

euphemistically (107) in a polite and socially acceptable manner

euphonious (22) melodious

euphoria (25) exaggerated feeling of well-being

euphoric (20, 92) bliss

evanescent (21, 140) quickly vanishing

exacerbate (51, 122) worsen

exasperation (64) frustration

excruciating (55, 58) intensely painful

execrable (22) awful

executed (31, 39) carried out

exhibitionistic (75) showing off

exhilaration (20, 44, 127) cheerful excitement

exhorting (17) urging

exodus (126) mass departure

expended (33) used up

exploits (67, 74, 98, 107) deeds / accomplishments

expressly (72) specifically

exquisite (91) superb

extenuating (67) justifying

extol (107) praise

extortion (3) intimidating pressure

extricate (16) liberate

exuberant (67, 74, 112) joyfully excited

exultation (67, 95) triumphant joyfulness

fabrication (140) artistic assembly

façade (51, 130) false appearance / cover up

facetious (17) humorous but silly / clumsy or inappropriate attempt to inject humor

fair damsel (65) see **fair maiden**

fair maiden (83) beautiful woman

familial (126) family-like

famished (27) very hungry

fanciful (3, 91) wildly imaginative

fancy (31, 44, 89, 105) showy / sudden notion

fanfare (16, 133) fancy display / scene

fateful (110, 140) critically decisive

fathom (7, 41) comprehend

fatigue (37) exhaustion

fatigued (33) tired

fatuous (7) foolish

fealty (84) loyalty

fearful (49, 52) afraid

fecund (31) fertile

feeble (56, 125) weak

feigned (64) pretended

felicity (67) joyfulness

fellowship (115) companionship

fend (15, 21, 62) manage

ferocity (56) unbearable intensity

ferret (out) (101) search out / dig out

festering (9) developing and growing

fettered (2) chained

fey (49, 98) supernatural / unreal

fiasco (133) disastrous failure

fisticuffs (122) fist-fight

flamboyant (89) elaborate and showy

fledgling (22) young / inexperienced

fledgling (27) novice

fleeting (44, 140) passing swiftly

flexing (7, 36) moving and contracting muscles

flippant (7) disrespectful

flourish (17, 110) grow and prosper

fluoresced (49) emitted light

focal (126) central

foe (17) enemy / opponent

foil (89) prevent the success of

folly (7) foolishness

foolhardy (15) recklessly bold

foolproof (83) not capable of allowing error

foraged (63) searched

forays (7) sudden attacks

forbidding (6) threateningly hostile

forefathers (7) ancestors

forge (76) give shape to

foster (67) harbor / maintain

fostered (64) promoted

frank (29) honest and openly direct

frayed (98) strained

frenetically (15) frantically

frequenting (49) attending regularly

fretting (31) worrying

friction (121) conflict

frills (91) decorative trimmings

frivolously (3) in a silly, foolish manner

frugally (22) in a stingy way

fruition (16) fulfillment

fugitive (89, 133) runaway

fugitive (20) short-lived

fury (9, 113, 122) rage / force

Gandhi (119) Indian political and spiritual leader

garbled (121) distorted, unclear / unintelligible

garish (76) tastelessly showy

garrulous (6) socially talkative

gawk (103) stare at stupidly or in wonder

germane (7) relevant

gingerly (60) carefully

gist (7, 16, 81) main idea / point

glared (52) stared angrily

glean (133) gather

gleefully (64, 133) merrily / joyfully

globally (71) worldwide

glowered (51, 88) stared angrily

gnawed (11) tormented constantly

goaded (31) spurred / urged on

god-forsaken (128) awful

Goliath (3) [Bible] a giant

gorge (64) stuff / fill to excess

grandeur (92) greatness

grandiose (112) magnificent

graphic (15) vivid

grated (2) rubbed irritatingly

gratitude (30) deep thankfulness and appreciation

gratuitous (133) free

grave (52) serious

grim (7, 27) stern / cruel

grit (3) courage

groggily (100) dazed / in a stunned manner

grovel (9) crawl (as in a display of self-worthlessness)

guise (11, 21) assumed (often, false) appearance

gulled (123) duped / tricked

gyrate (21, 54. 140) turn / spin around

halcyon (40, 138) peaceful

half-stupor (37) dazed state

hallowed (62) sacred

hallucinogenic (56) causing delusions

harbored (62) sheltered

haunt (20) frequented place

haven (21) refuge

headstrong (5) stubborn

heatedly (126) angrily

heed (46, 83) close attention

heedlessly (96) carelessly

heralding (43) announcing

Herculean (49) powerful

heuristic (3) rhetorical

hibernated (1007) lay dormant

hindrance (2) obstacle

Hiroshima (72) Japanese city that was the target of WW II atomic bomb attack

histrionics (51) theatrical drama

hitherto (16) until this time

honing (76) sharpening

hoodwinked (100) misled by trickery

hortatory (100) urging

hostility (80, 105, 112, 122) unfriendly feelings

hulking (49) massive

humble (9) humiliating

Humphrey Bogart (31) prominent 1940s - 1950s actor

hygienic (39) relating to health and cleanliness

hypocritical (128) saying one thing but then doing something contrary

hysteria (115) intense emotionalism, esp. of fear

iconoclast (8) revolutionary dissenter

iconoclastic (69) rebelliously dissenting

ideological (126) relating to ideals

ideology (64, 119, 122) fundamental beliefs

idiosyncratic (21) peculiar

idle (7) useless / meaningless

ill will (62) bitter feelings

illuminated (13) glowed

illusion (64, 140) false perception of reality

illusion (98) false vision

illusive (3) deceptive

imbroglio (51) entanglement

imbue (115) fill / saturate

immemorial (113) ancient

immense (43) huge

immersed (49, 63, 80, 114, 136) absorbed deeply

imminent (6) happening soon

immobile (56) unable to move

immortalized (136) made immortal / remembered forever

impasse (119) situation / position from which there is no escape

impassioned (110) passionate

impassivity (115) lack of emotion

impel (17, 100) urge forward / propel

impending (56, 71, 98) approaching

imperious (9, 113) domineering

impetuous (15) impulsive

impetus (17) stimulus

impish (110) mischievous

implied (11) suggested

implored (98) begged urgently

imposing (37) awesome

impotence (99) powerlessness

impregnating (43) permeating

impressed (7, 25, 65) favorably affected

impressed (89) stamped firmly in the mind

improvise (87) create or devise something offhand

inadvertently (92) unintentionally

incapacitating (43, 60, 99) crippling

incarceration (40) imprisonment

incendiary (6, 107, 119) inflammatory

incessant (44) endless

incidental (62) by chance

incite (6) provoke / arouse

incompetence (72) ineffectiveness

inconspicuously (21, 43, 63, 89) not seeking notice from others

incorporated (105) included

incredulously (30) skeptically and in disbelief

incriminating (92) blaming / relating to criminal activity

indefatigable (46) tireless

indifferent (25, 99, 112, 125) unconcerned / uninterested

indignant (9) resentful

indignation (49, 67) strong displeasure

indiscretion (3) thoughtlessness

indispensable (33) essential

indomitable (69) unconquerably

induce (17, 43) coax

indulge (64) oblige

ineffable (112) indescribable

ineffectual (52) without decisive effect

ineluctable (107) inescapable

inevitable (40, 94, 121) unavoidable / inescapable

inexorably (43) relentlessly

infallible (98) indestructible

inferno (37) oven / fiery pit

inferred (122) reasoned / concluded

infuriated (119) enraged

infuse (46, 61, 101) inspire

ingenuous (106) unsophisticated

ingested (99) swallowed

ingratiatingly (21) charmingly

iniquities (64) injustice

initiate (65, 75, 85) begin / originate

injudicious (123) unwise

innocuous (7, 122) harmless

innovatively (43) newly and creatively

innuendos (17) indirect (usually negative) references and comments / hints and rumors

innumerable (43) countless

inquietude (100) restlessness / uneasiness

inquiry (7) request

inquisitive (79, 112) curious

inscrutable (16) incomprehensible

inseparable (6) always together

insinuation (11) hint / suggestion

insouciance (44) lighthearted unconcern

insouciant (115) carefree and indifferent

instantaneous (43, 54) immediate

insubordinate (9) disobedient

insuperable (99) insurmountable

insurgent (64) rebellious

insurrection (69) outbreaks against authority

intact (55, 85) undamaged

intangible (87) not concrete

integral (49, 115) essential

integrity (17, 126) moral character

intemperate (11) unrestrained

intensifying (119) becoming more intense

intent (33, 126) determined / insistent

intently (128) firmly fixed

interjected (6, 46, 70) inserted / added in

interlude (33) pause

interposed (17, 85) interrupted / interjected intrusively

interrogating (81) questioning

intervened (74) stepped in

intimacy (106) closeness

intimate (1, 37, 62, 106, 138) close and deeply personal

intimated (11) hinted suggestion

intimidation (9) causing fear (as by threatening)

intolerable (43) unbearable

intoxicating (20) stimulating

intransigent (87) steadfast

intrepidly (15) fearlessly

introspective (13) self-analyzing

invasive (34) intruding

inveighing (64) railing / criticizing

inveigling (21) enticing

invert (87) reverse

invigorated (62) refreshed and enlivened

invincible (11) unconquerable

inviolate (62) sacred

invocation (69) call

involuted (120) complicated and unclear

irately (88) angrily

ironically (56) in an unusual and incongruous manner

irrelevant (1) unimportant

irreparably (126) irreversibly

irrepressible (22, 100) unstoppable

irreversible (126) unchangeable

irrevocable (43, 134) irreversible

jargon (119) meaningless language

jargon (25) specialized language

jaunty (18) buoyant / lively

jeering (17) mocking / ridiculing remarks

jeopardize (3, 18, 126) put in danger (of loss)

jeremiad (71) mournful complaint

jest (14, 34) humor / silliness

jocose (11) joking

jocular (41) humorous

jolting (34) shaking

Joseph Mengele (11) notorious WW II Nazi

juncture (134) critical point in time

jutting (96) extending

juvenile (3, 15) childish / immature

juvenile (83) designated for minors

juvenile (89) young

juxtaposed (87) placed side by side

Karl Marx (127) 19th century German revolutionary

keenly (76) perceptively

kindle (6, 17, 119) fuel / arouse or excite

kindred spirits (107) close friends ("soul mates")

kinship (14) close relationship

kismet (67) fate

labyrinthine (136) intricate

laced (105) flavored

lacerated (96) cut roughly

lackadaisical (109) unenthusiastic / uninterested

laconic (76) concise

languid (33) weak

languid (125) inert / spiritless

languishing (2) deteriorating

lark (27) escapade / fling

latent (9, 113, 122) concealed

latitude (76) freedom of direction / action

lavished (2) bestowed generously

leavening (101) lightening up

legacy (106) something handed down to a future generation

Leonardo da Vinci (7) multitalented 15th century painter

lethargically (37) sluggishly

liberation (6) freedom

license (72) freedom

licentious (109) sexually unrestrained

likelihood (6) strong possibility

linger (11, 37) remain

literally (25, 33) exactly / true to fact

lone (56, 83) only / single

long (11, 62, 96, 102) desire

loquacious (67) talkative

lordly (9, 113) domineering

low-key (83) restrained

LSD (106) a hallucinogenic drug

lucidly (9) clearly understood

ludicrous (7) absurd and ridiculous

lugubrious (56) gloomy

luminary (105) celebrity

lush (61) abundant

lust (64) intense desire

lustrous (91) dazzling

luxuriate (43) delight

machinations (43, 89) schemes

macho (94, 100) masculine (usually exaggeratedly so)

maelstrom (58) whirlpool

maitre d' (25) headwaiter

majestic (91) magnificent and elegant

malady (58) ailment

malaise (11) mental uneasiness / general weakness

malcontent (6) a person dissatisfied with conditions as they are

malevolent (34) sinister

malice (36) desire to injure / harm

malleable (78) shapeable

mammoth (85) enormous

mandated (31) ordered

manifold (83) numerous

manipulated (21) managed shrewdly or deviously

manifestos (127) declarations of beliefs, goals and purposes

mannerism (21) distinctive behavioral trait

manumit (13) liberate

martyr (83) person who suffers openly in behalf of a belief / cause

marvel (44, 84) feel curious astonishment

masterful (103) excellently done

masterminded (107) planned

matronly (98) befitting a mature woman

maverick (7) independent, apart from the herd

meager (17) lacking fullness / richness

mealymouthed (11) cowardly insincere

meandered (11) wandered

mediocrity (17, 107, 138) lack of excitement and interest

mediocrity (69) indifference

mellifluence (22) sweet harmony

melodic (51) musical

melodrama (15, 60) exaggerated drama

mementos (138) souvenirs / reminders of the past

mendacious (100) untruthful

mentors (69, 91) teachers

merit (7) excellence / value

metaphorically (56) poetically

meticulous (60, 87) extremely careful / precisely detailed

metropolis (2) a large, busy (and often, capital) city

metropolitan (107) relating to a major city

mettle (11) courage

migration (43) journey

milestone (87) significant historical event

millennium (89) one thousand years (in context: a very long time)

mindlessly (1) without thinking

miscreant (89) evildoer

misguided (72, 123, 136) misdirected

Mission Impossible (83) movie/tv show containing plots of danger and intrigue

mistletoe (110) Christmas plant

mock (64) imitating

moderation (74) reasonableness

modish (105) fashionable

momentous (43, 134) extremely important

Monet (87) French painter

monotone (34) single-toned, without variation

moot (3, 64) unresolvable

mordant (107) sarcastic

mortal (44) earthly / human

mortal (98) extreme

motif (85) theme / idea

motivated (2) stimulated

motley (69) diverse

mousily (11) timidly

mulled over (6, 67) pondered

multifarious (91) diverse

multitude (20, 67) large number

mum (83) not saying a word

mundane (17) day-to-day

mused (74) pondered at length

muster (3, 24) assemble / gather together

mute (15) silence

muted (140) unable to speak/ speechless

mutinied (40) rebelled

mutual (113) shared

myriad (116) numerous

mystical (126) mysterious

Nagasaki (72) Japanese city that was the target of WW II atomic bomb attack

naïvely (101) sincerely but without informed judgment

naïveté (123) innocence

Nam (128) Viet Nam

narcissism (119) overconcern and interest in oneself

naught (60) nothing

nauseous (56) sick

nebulous (100) hazy / vague

nemesis (11) opponent / rival (often, a superior one)

neophyte (103) novice

nettled (87) annoyed

nigh (22) near

nirvana (63) state of bliss

nomadic (128) wandering

nonchalantly (20, 40, 115) in a cool, unconcerned manner

nondescript (63) inconspicuous

nonplussed (65) baffled / perplexed

notable (6) exceptional

notion (5, 76, 87, 126) idea / conception

notoriety (107) an unfavorable reputation

nuance (87) subtle shade

nudged (105) pushed gently against

nugatory (9) worthless

nurture (31) develop / promote

obligatory (106) morally / legally required

oblivion (55) a state of forgetfulness

oblivious (95, 110) totally unaware

obsessed (40, 64) fixated

odoriferous (58) scented

offensive (76) insulting

ogled (94) glanced at amorously

omnipresence (109) being everywhere and observing everything

opportune (48) favorable / suitable

oppressive (37) burdensome

opted (63, 113) chose

optimism (70, 133) positive hopefulness

ordeal (115) severe / painful experience

ornate (92) elaborate

ostentation (89) showy display

ostentatious (112) extravagantly showy

ostracized (8) banished

otiose (17) purposeless

outraged (119) infuriated

outset (89) start

outspoken (7) honest and open

outwitted (8) outsmarted

overhead (76) operating expenses

overt (109, 122) obvious

painstaking (91) extremely careful

palatable (63) appetizing

pall (56) covering / shadow

palliate (99) relieve

palpably (87) noticeably

pang (102, 126) sudden, sharp pain

panoramic (31) scenic

paragon (8) contradiction

paralysis (96) state of being paralyzed

paramount (21) foremost

parsimonious (76) stingy / frugal

passionate (65, 75, 127) emotionally intense

pastel (72) soft and delicate

pathetically (98) miserably and pitifully

patrons (56) protectors

pawns (21) people used to further the purposes of another

pedagogically (78) in an instructional / teaching manner

pedestrian (27) person walking

peer (56, 61, 87, 116) look searchingly

peers (17, 100) fellow classmates / associates

penchant (15) fondness

pensive (31, 61) dreamily and thoughtful

perception (20, 121) observation

perchance (63) perhaps

perdition (40, 98) eternal damnation

peregrination (16, 115) journey

peregrine (134) wandering

peremptory (9, 43) absolute and without debate or argument

perfunctorily (20) superficially

peril (33, 71) danger

perilous (25, 136) hazardous

periodically (27) occasionally

peripatetic (107) traveling

permeated (55) spread throughout

pernicious (51, 96) dangerous

perplexing (3, 31) puzzling

perturbed (70) greatly disturbed

petrified (96) scared stiff / frozen in fear

petulant (8) irritable and sulking

picaresque (16, 115) adventuresome

Picasso (91) Spanish artist

picayune (119) valueless

pilfering (21) stealing

pine (105) crave

piquant (40) stimulating

pitfalls (83) hazards

pithy (76) concise and meaningful

pivotal (134) crucially important as a turning point

pixie-like (110) mischievous

placid (29, 44, 61) calm and peaceful

plaintive (61) mournful

plastic (140) artificial

platitudes (130) overused and meaningless remarks

plaudits (101) praise

plebeian (44) common / ordinary

plight (7, 69, 79, 122) distressed and unfortunate situation

plug nickel (85) nickel made from inferior metal

plumbed (2, 114) penetrated and examined

plush (30) richly deep / thick

poltroons (11) cowards

polychromatic (103) multicolored

ponder (13, 17, 31, 56, 98, 113) reflect on / meditate on

pontificate (64) speak pompously

portent (98) omen

portentous (71) ominous

postured (98) standing

potency (56, 110) power

potent (43, 60) powerful

precarious (25, 51, 69) dangerously uncertain

precarious (87) dangerous and insecure / risky

precipitate (113) hasten / bring on

precipitately (3, 92) hastily

precipitous (196) steep

predator (51, 96) hunter

predicament (25, 31, 40, 116, 136) difficult, troublesome situation

predominated (49) ruled

prelude (113) introduction

premature (25, 95) early-occurring

preoccupation (1) focused attention and thought

preoccupied (44, 127) absorbed in thought

prerequisite (105) requirement

prerogative (79) choice

prescribing (78) ordering

presumption (112) assumption made beforehand

presumptuous (25, 95) overstepping one's bounds/ being too forward

presupposing (114) assuming in advance

prevail (69) triumph

prevailed (113) are in control

prevalent (21, 69) widespread / widely existing

prey (33) food (specifically, a victim of attack from a predator)

prey (11) victim

primary (33, 94, 126) main

prime (76) primary

pristine (61) pure and untouched

probing (7, 20, 81) search

problematic(al) (92, 134) uncertain

procured (22) obtained

prodding (110) urge encouragingly

prodigious (91) immense

prodigy (76) genius

proffered (17) offered

profound (69) intense

progeny (60) offspring

prolific (76) productive

prominence (34) noticeably

promontory (96) high hedge overlooking the sea

pronounced (96) obvious

propaganda (67, 107) publicity promoting a cause or belief

prophecy (78) prediction

propitiate (13, 52) appease

prosaic (17) unimaginative

proselyte (64) convert

proselytize (71) attempt at converting (to a cause / belief)

protégé (69, 72) a person who is under the support and protection of another

protracting (22) extending

protruding (15) sticking out

proverbial (136) containing a practical message

providential (56) fortunate

provocation (51) creating anger / resentment

provocative (6, 81, 121) stimulating

provoked (112) stirred / aroused

promontory (96) high ledge overlooking the sea

pronounced (96) obvious

psychedelic (106) producing hallucinations

puerile (3, 100) childish

puissance (11) power / might

pun (2) humorous and clever word play

puny (52) tiny

purloin (21) steal

pusillanimous (11) cowardly

Pyrrhic victory (8) victory gained at too great a cost

quaffing (60) guzzling

qualified (83) restricted

quarry (96) prey

quasi-mantra (69) resembling a mantra (mantra: a mystical invocation)

quell (56) subdue

query (3, 7, 29, 64) question (to solve a doubt)

quest (44, 71, 126) search

queue (31, 76) braid of hair

quipped (14) remarked in a witty manner

quirky (14) eccentric

quiver (29) shake

quixotic (40, 126) idealistic / unrealistic

quotidian (3) daily

racked (55) afflicted

radiance (37) shining

rampant (107) widespread

rancor (113) bitterness

rankled (17) irritated

rapacious (64, 136) greedy / hungry

rapscallion (21) rascal

rapture (65) ecstasy

rash (15) reckless and without careful consideration

rationale (14, 43, 122) body of reasons supporting a belief

rationalization (109) justification (often as an excuse or accommodating explanation)

ravenously (33) hungrily

Reagan (69) former U.S. president

realize (44, 63) accomplish / make real

realm (3) domain

reassurance (15) encouragement / cheering up

reassure (29, 74, 81, 136) restore confidence

rebukes (9) scolds

recalcitrance (7, 138) stubborn rebelliousness

recherché (60) rare and superior

recitations (64) a memorized speech

recollect (89) remember

recompense (51) a repayment for something earlier done / suffered

reconciliation (114) restoring to friendship or unity

recurred (49, 61) occurred again / continued repeatedly

redeem (126) rescue / reform or set straight

red-handed (91) in the act

redolent (40) reminiscent

redoubtable (52) awesome

refuge (27, 98) shelter from danger and trouble

refugees (36) runaways

regal (39) royal

regalement (60) amusement

reins (3) restrains

rejuvenation (43) restoring youthful vigor and energy

rekindle (43, 69, 95) reawaken / restart

relativistic (14) based on the theory of relative existence

relentless (37) mercilessly persistent

relevant (3, 69, 115, 125) appropriate

relief (96) land characteristics (elevation, etc.)

relish (25, 60) enjoy greatly

rely (123) depend

remorseful (9) sad

remote (76) separated / set apart / not in the main view

remuneration (9) payment

renaissance (107) renewal / rebirth

rendezvous (64, 109) prearranged meeting

Renoir (87) French painter

renowned (106) well known

repartee (8) witty conversation

repast (60) meal

repercussions (25, 83) effects and consequences

replenish (42) renew

replete (16, 83, 105) abundantly filled

repose (60, 80) peace / calmness

repositories (78) places for storage

reprehensible (72) shameful

reprising (118) repeating

resentment (67) bad feelings

reservations (70, 113) doubts

reserve (29, 62) self-restraint / shyness

residual (67) remaining

resign (31, 56) give in without resistance

resolute (76) firmly determined

resolution (5) firm determination

resolution (119) solution to a problem

resolve (113, 138) find a solution to

resolve (81, 87) firm determination

resonance (33) echoing

resonate (33, 134) give off a sound

resourceful (87) inventive / creative

respective (122) separate or individual

respite (5) interval / rest

resplendent (91, 112) dazzling / sparkling

restive (138) disobedient

resurrect (112) bring back to life

retain (61, 103, 107) hold on to

retaliations (122) vengeful actions / deeds to pay back or get even

reticence (112) shyness

retorted (119) replied sharply

retribution (8) punishment (as revenge)for a wrongdoing

retrogression (69) going backward and (usually) to a worse condition

revel (43, 63) delight greatly

revelation (122, 126) discovery

reverberations (58) echoing aftereffects

revered (9, 69) respected and feared

reverie (63) daydream

revitalized (33, 44) renewed in energy

rhapsodic (63) ecstatic

rhetorical (3) verbal ornate though materially unanswerable

rife (43) abundant

rift (121,126) split or separation / break in friendly relations

rigidly (98) strictly

ritualistic (43) ceremonially or customarily repeated

rival (61) equal

riveted (16) engrossed

riveting (67) spellbinding

roguish (44) mischievous

rouse (6) awaken

row (13) noisy quarrel

rueful (60) sad

ruffled (99) irritated

ruminate (31, 60, 63, 114) meditate at length / ponder

rummage (91) search hastily

rural (107) countryside

rut (74) monotonous routine

saccharine (67) sweet

sacrament (43) ritual

sacrosanct (62) sacred

safeguard (29) protect

sagacious (113) wise

salacious (110) obscene

sallow (56) pale / sickly

salubrious (43) healthful

salvation (3, 17, 100, 106) means of liberation

sanguine (87) optimistic

sapid (15) tasty

satchel (134) shoulder bag

saturnine (112) gloom

saunter (11) stroll

savior (29) rescuer

savor (43, 95, 98) enjoy

savory (22, 63) tasty

saw (113) familiar saying

scamper (94, 128) rush

scathing (9) bitterly severe

scenario (17, 55, 60) developing plot

schism (122) rift

scintillating (18) sparkling

score (40) a group of twenty

scouring (109) searching through

scowled (27) expressed with an angry frown

scrawny (52) skinny

scrimped (76) be frugal

scrutinizing (89) examining closely

scurried (40) hurried

scuttlebutt (40) gossip

secluded (29) isolated / kept apart

secured (51, 128) firmly fastened / closed

sedating (55) calming

sedative (99) calming medication

seditiously (69) rebelliously

seductive (17, 110) tempting

sedulously (107) diligently

self-effected (138) done by himself

self-possession (89) confidence / composure

semblance (25) appearance

sensationalistic (67) exaggerated / shocking

sensationalized (133) presented exaggeratedly

sensuously (17) sexually appealing

sententious 64 moralizing

seraphic (62) angelic

serendipitously (95) fortunately

serene (61) peaceful

serenity (58, 109) peacefulness

servitude (2) slavery

sever (83) separate / break off

shackled (13, 44) chained

Shangri-la (63) imaginary paradise on earth

sheepishly (78) in an embarrassed manner

shell-shocked (98) psychologically unnerved (as from the experience of war)

shibboleth (17) pet phrase

shimmering (110) sparkling

shoddy (87) inferior

shortcomings (138) faults

Shylock (51) [Shakespeare] a creditor who sought a pound of flesh as recompense for past debts

sinister (15, 25, 52, 96, 122) threatening trouble / harm

sit-ins (106, 107) organized protests

sizable (89) large

skimpy (29) scanty / inadequate

slumber (81) sleep

slumberous (34) sleepy

smug (20, 64) complacent / self-satisfied

snickered (21, 65) laughed in a sly, sarcastic or snide manner

snide (103) sarcastic / insulting

sober (34, 63) rational

sobering (55, 69, 102) causing one to become sober / bringing to one a serious understanding

soberly (6) seriously

solace (49) comfort

solar (43) coming from the sun

solemnity (16) seriousness

solemnly (79) in a serious and honest manner

solicitude (58) concern

solidarity (69, 126) unity

solitary (56, 96) single / secluded

solitude (54, 61) isolation

somnolent (33) drowsy

sooth (21, 138) truth

soothingly (34) calmingly

sophisticated (21, 91) intricate / advanced

sophomoric (3) immature

soporific (34) extremely drowsy

soporific (99) inducing sleep

sordidly (67) vulgarly / cheaply

specious (100) superficially

specter (98) apparition / ghost

speculating (31, 105) pondering

spires (96) pointed shoots

splayed (95) spread out

splendor (63, 110) brilliance / magnificence

spontaneity (109) naturalness

spontaneous (7) natural

sportive (65) playful

sprightly (125) lively

spurious (100) false / bogus

spurned (62) rejected scornfully

spruced (62) neat in appearance

squabble (114) quarrel

stable (114) sturdy / secure

stagnating (15) becoming sluggish / dull/ not moving

staid (16) sober / serious

stalkers (96) predators

stark (29) bare

starkly (134) plain / absolutely

status quo (17, 69) current state of affairs

staunchly (76) unwavering

steadfast (56) steady and uncompromising

steeped (110) saturated

stemmed (128) derived

stentorian (33) loud

sterile (33) sanitary / barren

stern (7) harsh and expressing displeasure

stifle (13) hold back / restrain

stimulant (20, 58) substance that stimulates activity or sensual awareness

stimulate (27, 78, 106) arouse

stipulations (31) requirements

stock (11) common / ordinary

stoking (65) stirring up

straightforward (41, 112) direct

stray (33) wander

strewn (125) scattered

stricken (99) afflicted

stripling (92) young

strive (3, 138) make a strong effort

stultifying (100) repressive

stupefaction (110) shock

stupefied (56) stunned

stupor (37, 56) a dazed or stunned condition

stygian (40) hellish

subdue (98) overpower

subdued (34, 85, 105, 112) toned down / refraining from showiness

subjugate (56) enslave

subjugate (3, 99) overpower

sublime (54) glorious / superb

submission (9, 58) yielding to the power of another

submitting (17) surrendering

subscribe (78, 123) consent

subsequently (133) thereafter

subservience (31) servile obedience

subsistence (17) minimal existence

substantial (16) solid and sound

subtle (7, 103) not obvious or direct / faint but noticeable

suburb (49) outlying part of the city

subversive (69, 107) undermining and malicious / underhanded and socially destructive

subversive (89) seeking to undermine

succor (56) assistance in time of need

succulent (25) juicy

suffice (105) be adequate

sufficient (21) adequate

suffusing (43) saturating

Sugar Ray Leonard (11) 1980s boxing champion

sultry (110) sweltering

summarily (122) immediately

summit (96) top

sundry (17, 67) assorted

superficial (51, 114) not serious or deep

superfluous (115) unnecessary

supernal (61) heavenly

supine (31) lying on one's back

supple (84) gracefully flexible

suppress (65, 107) stifle

suppression (22) censorship

supremacy (9) supreme authority

surly (27) rude

surmised (52) figured / determined without deeper thought

surmounting (11) overcoming

surfeit (107) excess

surreptitiously (138) in a sneaky manner

surrogate (103) substitute

surveillance (21) close observation

surveying (44, 131) looking over

sustenance (22, 63) nourishment

sustenance (107) livelihood

swarthy (34) dark-skinned

sweltering (37) oppressively hot

sybaritic (40) luxurious and pleasurable

Sylvester Stallone (49) 1980s "tough guy" actor

symbiosis (114) coexistence

symmetry (91) balanced form of construction

syringe (52) medical needle for injecting fluids into the body

tacit (29, 80) unspoken, yet clearly communicated

tangent (67) digression

tangible (87, 138) real / touchable

tantalizing (1) charmingly tempting

tantamount (92) equivalent in meaning

teeming (72, 105) abundant

telling (56) forcefully revealing

telltale (138) revealing

tempered (44, 55, 109) calmed or moderated / controlled or softened

tempest (65) storm

tempestuously (79) violently

temporal (6) temporary

tenets (64) fundamental beliefs

tentative (125) uncertain

tenuous (114, 122) flimsy and on a weak support ("hanging by a thread")

testament (69) tribute

testimonial (112) formal statement

threadbare (123) overused / outdated

thriftiness (43) conserving in spending

thrive (69) flourish

timbre (22, 34) tonal quality of a sound

timely (56) well timed

timid (30) shy

tintinnabulation (5) ringing / jingling

titan (49) giant

token (2, 65) symbol

tomfoolery (7) foolish / silly behavior

topographic (96) relating to physical land features

torridly (65) hotly

torturous (115) painfully agonizing

tranquil (17, 80, 100, 122) calm / peaceful

transformed (69, 91, 103, 105) changed in appearance

transient (21) temporary

transmuting (87) changing

transpired (94, 110) came to happen / occurred

traverse (61, 110, 138) travel along / move across

trek (17, 43, 136, 138) difficult travel / journey

trepidation (25, 109) nervousness / fear

trifle (126) little bit

trinkets (125) odds and ends

trite (87, 125) overused and unimaginative / meaningless and uninteresting

triumphal (112) victorious

truant (49) absent (from school) without permission

truants (49) students not attending school

trying (21) difficult

tryst (112) secret engagement

twinge (41, 62, 118) pang / emotional pang

tyro (69) beginner / newcomer

ubiquitous (109) appearing everywhere

unbounded (7, 84) limitless

unbridled (96, 113) wild and uncontrolled

uncanny (125) weird / strange

unceremoniously (7) rudely abrupt

uncircumspect (92) not vigilant

unconstrained (89) limitless

undermine (95, 118) destroy by wearing away at the foundation

undertaking (94) setting about to do

undulating (56) moving in a wave-like manner

uneasiness (112) restlessness

uneasy (115) uncomfortable

uneasy (33) upset

unencumbering (16) free from burden

unequivocal (110) definite / unquestionable or undeniable

unfettered (100) free

unflinching (94) not cowering

unhampered (89) unobstructed

unhindered (31) unobstructed

uninhibited (95) outgoing / outspoken

unison (in unison) (1) together

unmitigated (140) absolute

unmuddle (79) remove confusion from

unnerved (98) stripped of courage / strength

unobtrusively (122) modestly / reservedly

unorthodox (64) not traditionally acceptable

unpretentiously (100) naturally

unqualified (24) unrestricted

unrelenting (58) persisting

unremitting (17, 96) constant

unrest (69) discontent

unshackled (13) free

unsung (105) unacknowledged

untrammeled (31) unrestricted

unwitting (21) not knowing / aware

upstanding (89) morally upright

urban (107) relating to the city

usurped (25) snatched

utopian (16, 119) idealistic

utter (65, 98) complete

utter (30, 43, 62, 140) speak

vagabond (31, 40) wandering

vaguely (33, 89) unclearly

vain (in vain) (55) without success

vaingloriously (20) conceitedly

vanquish (98) conquer

variables (87, 89) elements subject to change

vast (31, 76, 127) very great

vast (61) very large

vaunt (89) brag about

veiled (22) masked / concealed

venal (64) open to bribery

veneer (49) outward appearance

vengeance (22) revenge

verdant (61) green

verge (122, 127) edge / border

veritable (37) actual

vertigo (56) dizziness

verve (25) artistic spirit

veterans (69) people with noteworthy experience

viands (60) food

vibrant (105) vivid

vicariously (112, 123) indirectly

victor (49) winner

Viet Nam (69, 106) scene of U.S. involvement during 1960s-1970s conflict

vigilant (51) alert

vigor (13) energy

villainous (89) befitting a criminal

vim (99) vitality

virile (13) masculine

virtually (100, 109) practically / essentially

visceral (107) instinctive

visionary (16) unrealistic

visitation (61) official visit

vista (31) scenic view

vital (37) essential

vitality (99) energy

vitriolic (121) bitterly antagonistic

vituperations (64) scoldings

vivid (62) lifelike

vivid (87, 114) lively / energetic

vivid (138) memorably impressive

vivified (67, 112) added liveliness to

vociferous (64) noisy

vogue (11) style

void (56, 106) emptiness

volatile (113) easily exploding / becoming violent

volition (56) free will

volley (7) barrage

voraciously (60) ravenously

vortex (58) whirlpool

vulnerability (56, 83) openness to injury, criticism / attack

wafted (22) floated

waif (20, 27, 115) homeless and helpless person (usually, a child)

wanderlust (31, 100) desire to travel

waning (17) declining

wanton (109) lustful

warrant (115) justify

wary (115) cautiously watchful

Watergate (64, 107) 1970s example of political corruption

wavered (33) swayed

wayfarer (133) traveler

weary (80, 106, 107, 133) tired / fatigued

weathering (85) surviving

wee (37) very early

welfare (96) health and happiness

welling (78) filling

wheedling (21) coaxing

whet (6, 43, 91) stimulate

whim (15, 31, 40, 119) sudden idea / wish

whimpered (52) sobbed softly or weakly

whimsical (5) fanciful

whirred (22) fluttered and buzzed

willful (112, 128) intentional

wily (21) cunning

wistfully (102) wishfully

witticism (41) clever remark

wizened (22) shriveled

woeful (76, 123) miserable

wrangled (119) argued

wrench (52) twist

wrest (3) obtain

wry (96) twisted / cynical

Xanadu (49) mythical city

yearned (54, 100, 106, 115) desired strongly / craved

zeal (87) enthusiasm

THREE STEPS TO INCREASE VOCABULARY
USING THE HI-LITE SERIES CFR® METHOD

1. **CONFRONT WORDS** in this book that you don't know.

    (Highlight them for added emphasis)

2. **FAMILIARIZE** yourself with their definition.

    (Use the helpful *Glossary*)

3. **REINFORCE** the definitions of newly-acquired words through additional READING.

    (There are two other books in this vocabulary-building trilogy!)

CONFRONT

FAMILIARIZE

REINFORCE
(BY READING)

VERBAL PROFICIENCY IS THE KEY TO BETTER WRITING AND CLEARER COMMUNICATION